SPECIAL DIET COOKBO

ASTHMA & ECZE

SPECIAL DIET COOKBOOKS

ASTHMA & ECZEMA

Easy and delicious calcium rich recipes to relieve the problems of milk intolerance, which may also be helpful for rhinitis, sinusitis, catarrh, urticaria, joint pain and irritable bowel syndrome.

Carol Bennett

THORSONS PUBLISHING GROUP

First published 1989

British Library Cataloguing in Publication Data

Bennett, Carol
    Asthma and eczema: easy and delicious
    calcium-rich meals to relieve the
    problems of milk intolerance
    I. Title   II. Series
    641.5'632

ISBN 0-7225-1821-8

Text illustrations by Juanita Puddifoot

Published by Thorsons Publishers Limited,
Wellingborough, Northamptonshire,
NN8 2RQ, England.

Typeset by Harper Phototypesetters Limited,
Northampton, England.
Printed in Great Britain by Bath Press,
Bath, Avon.

10 9 8 7 6 5 4 3 2

To my family, who tasted all the recipes.

ACKNOWLEDGEMENTS

I would like to thank Mrs Joan James, Mrs J. Kidd, Dr D.B. Long, Mrs Elaine Pieters, Dr Sue Southern, Mrs J. Thornton, Dr Hazel Tyler and the many others who gave me valuable assistance with this book.

CONTENTS

INTRODUCTION

I decided to write this cook book because it is the very thing I was looking for when I was confronted with the task of having to devise a milk-free diet for my son. At the time I didn't know where to begin, and the prospect of having to adapt my cooking for one child while at the same time suiting the rest of the family seemed extremely daunting. I simply did not have the time to prepare separate meals so I planned at the outset that we would all eat the same things. With a little trial and error it soon became apparent that I could make lasagne, quiche, moussaka, cheese sauces, etc., by substituting goat's or soya milk for cow's milk, and the ewe's milk Feta cheese for most cooking cheeses. As I became more confident I served these dishes to guests and was delighted to see that they had not noticed my substitutions. Patrick was not made to feel different because we were all on his 'special diet'.

Asthma, eczema, rhinitis, sinusitis, catarrh, urticaria, joint pain, and irritable bowel syndrome are just some of the ways in which a milk allergy can manifest itself. I am not in the position to advise anyone to alter his diet and I would strongly urge any reader to seek medical advice before excluding dairy products. However once a milk allergy, or more precisely a milk intolerance diagnosis, has been made, this book will help you. It gives practical advice on how to compensate for the lack of cow's milk products by using goat's or ewe's milk products and soya milk and how to make up for any calcium shortfall by eating more fish, dark green leafy vegetables, root vegetables, bread, almonds and certain fruits. The beauty of these foods is that they are valuable not only for their calcium but from a number of different nutritional viewpoints. By eating a good diet you will help to improve your health generally.

The inability to digest cow's milk in adult life is common among the non-white races. The cuisine enjoyed by the largest population in the world — the Chinese — does not include any dairy products. Clearly it is possible to eat a balanced diet without using cow's milk and its by-products. However, on the practical level, few people will have the single-mindedness or application to alter their diets so drastically. When making the change to a milk-free diet it is not necessary to make dramatic alterations in your eating habits. The recipes in this book allow you to eat the sort of foods most people enjoy, although many are made from slightly different ingredients. At the same time I hope the reader wil become more conscious of those foods which boost calcium levels in the diet, and will choose to eat more of them. Non-meat eaters who eat fish should not have difficulties in re-establishing a balanced diet, but vegetarians will have to rely more heavily on goat's and/or ewe's milk products.

Milk-allergic babies or very young children who are no longer being breast-fed require medical assistance. In the place of cow's milk a fortified soya milk formula or diluted and boiled goat's or sheep's milk may be prescribed. Ordinary soya milk must never be regarded as a replacement for cow's milk. The recipes in this book will be of some use for children who are toddlers and upwards, but parents can get more detailed counselling, as well as advice on possible mineral and vitamin supplementation, from a paediatrician. The guidance and recipes in this book will also be helpful to breast-feeding mothers whose babies are reacting to the dairy products in their own diets.

When at the age of twelve our son Patrick was put on a cow's milk-exclusion diet by his paediatrician in the hope that there would be an improvement in his asthma and eczema, the results were amazing. A child who had lately been coming last in races began to finish among the first two or three over the line. Instead of getting bronchitis with each cold and missing weeks of school at a time, he was able to shrug off colds in the normal way. The eczema, which had made his hands red and liable to split and crack in the winter, subsided to a slight, painless blush which disappeared altogether in the summer months. Best of all, he stopped using all of his inhalers and drugs.

My husband had suffered from asthma, rhinitis and hay fever as a child and in his mid-thirties he developed a duodenal ulcer. Patrick had the reverse: severe stomach and bowel problems from age two to three, rhinitis at about nine and asthma and eczema at eleven. Our younger boy had established a cycle from the age of four of hay fever in the summer and sinusitis in the winter and year-round catarrh. All three have benefited from a dairy product-free diet. It was when Patrick began to get bronchitis with each cold, associated with his asthma, that I became worried. His father had developed pneumonia five times when he was growing up, and I could see the pattern repeating itself in the next generation.

Patrick was very fortunate that the main cause of his asthma and eczema was eventually found to be dietary. If his illness had been triggered primarily by unavoidable atmospheric irritants there would have been no choice but to investigate ways of controlling the symptoms with drugs. Indeed the first consultant Patrick and I had seen was on the point of prescribing a daily dose of Intal, which is a medication designed to pre-empt breathing difficulties. But in the back of my mind, all I could think was that there must be a simpler alternative. I had read that food allergies were often a cause of asthma and eczema, so at our next hospital appointment I asked the registrar about it. His answer was, 'Oh, you don't want to get involved in exclusion diets. They're very difficult to follow and usually inconclusive. And in addition they make a child different from the other school children and so lead to social problems.' The attitude seemed to be that the degree of severity of my son's asthma and eczema did not warrant an exhaustive investigation since his symptoms could be adequately alleviated with medications and creams. In the end I sought a second opinion, as was our right under the National Health Service, and consulted a paediatrician at the Brompton Hospital. He immediately advised the elimination of all cow's milk and dairy products, as well as food containing azo dyes and benzoates, and any other foods we suspected. We were given long lists of food to avoid; in fact, what it amounted to was that Patrick was to have nothing but pure foods and no dairy products.

This was in 1984. Fortunately the trend since then has been towards eliminating potentially harmful chemicals from processed foods, but at that time I found it very difficult to find any tins or prepared foods that did not contain unacceptable colourings, flavourings or preservatives. When shopping for Patrick for the first time under the new regime I discovered to my shame that I had never really read the labels on food wrappings before. I suddenly realized there was room for improvement in all the family's diet, not just in Patrick's.

During the first month of Patrick's elimination diet we were waiting for his system to be cleansed of all traces of foods we suspected he was allergic to, but to which his body had, over a long period, become accustomed. Already his hands were clearing up. Then we 'challenged' Patrick with different foods to see if he exhibited any signs of allergy. An allergic reaction could take many forms, from something as vague as a stomach ache to a dramatic flaring up of the eczema. Sometimes we weren't sure, and we had to wait another week or two and try again. It took us four months of challenging to build up to the food we suspected the most, which is what we had been told to try last — milk. At first there was no reaction, but the next day, Patrick's hands went very red. Considering how clear his hands had been of eczema from the start of his new diet, we knew there was no doubt that Patrick was allergic to dairy products.

As soon as we felt sure that Patrick wasn't sensitive to a particular food he was allowed to eat it again, so his repertoire rapidly expanded from the initial very limited regime. Even at that difficult early stage his school coped admirably with his dinners. The only comment another child ever made when he saw Patrick eating a salad as the rest of the boys were tucking into macaroni cheese was rather funny: 'Why are you on a diet? You're thin already'! Because we were all on Patrick's diet at home, he didn't feel different. When we had guests I served only what I knew he could eat. Restaurants were all right because there was usually something that was acceptable, and parties weren't too bad because Patrick could see all the food and choose. The most difficult situation was being invited to someone else's house. Often our hostess knew of Patrick's allergies beforehand, and would even ring up to find out what to avoid, only to offer him Cheddar cheese sandwiches on the day, made specially with milk-free Granose margarine! Somehow it didn't seem to get through that no dairy products meant no cow's milk, butter, cheese, yogurt and cream.

As the weeks went by I was becoming concerned about the loss of calcium in the diet when dairy products are excluded. Patrick was having soya milk at the time, and I knew that soya milk had much less calcium than cow's milk. The dietitians at the Brompton Hospital were extremely supportive and helpful, and recommended some other sources, especially fish with bones and dark leafy vegetables. Patrick's paediatrician suggested trying goat's or ewe's milk products. He gave me the advice that although half the people who are allergic to cow's milk are allergic to goat's milk, hardly anyone is allergic to ewe's milk. Although I have yet to find a supplier of ewe's milk in my immediate area, I soon found that the Greek ewe's milk cheese, Feta, was available in the supermarket, as was Greek ewe's milk yogurt. Luckily these new foods had no ill effects on Patrick.

As a result of our own testing at home, we decided that Patrick was allergic to milk, some varieties of nuts, and peaches. Later he underwent a week of double-blind tests for chemical allergies at a London hospital, and reacted to one, E133, which is a red food colouring. His paediatrician told me that now Patrick's testing was finished he needed to avoid only those few things and he could go back to eating anything he liked. I looked horrified and asked, jokingly, if that meant he could eat foods with lots of additives. He replied that he could, but he and I both knew that Patrick's and my eyes had been opened, and we had become avid and careful readers of labels. That Christmas Patrick gave me Maurice Hanssen's *E for Additives* (Thorsons, 1984) to help me with my new hobby, looking up E numbers and checking them for harmful effects.

Having had such good results with Patrick we were surprised and pleased to find that avoiding dairy products, especially in the forms of cheese and butter, helped to improve my husband's duodenal ulcer. I began to wonder what could be done for our younger boy, so I made an appointment with a herbalist for Laurie, who by this time was 13. Aside from courses of antibiotics, conventional medicine hadn't been able to do much for the sinusitis he got repeatedly every winter. At our first visit the herbalist recommended eliminating milk. He explained that milk increases the mucus in the upper respiratory tract, which is why the advice not to drink milk during a cold is often given. Up to that point Laurie had still been drinking milk even though the rest of his food was dairy-product free. Once again, we could observe the differences when he stopped having milk. His catarrh improved, his voice sounded less nasal, and his skin became clear. That winter he caught colds, but for the first time in eight years he did not get sinusitis, and he has not had sinusitis since.

With the benefit of hindsight, I realize that given the familial pattern of allergies such as ours, it would have been better to withhold dairy products from our children's diets for as long as possible in infancy and early childhood. I often think that the fact that both my children were given bottles of cow's milk formula in hospital, even though I was breast-feeding them, may have triggered their allergies. In recent years the nursing staff in hospitals have become more aware of this problem, and will try to co-operate if the mother tells them that there is a history of milk allergy in the family.

This book has two aims: to give you recipes the whole family can eat when one of you is allergic to milk, and to explain how to get enough calcium on a milk-free diet. The recipes are mostly everyday cooking with an emphasis on speed of preparation, although there are some more elaborate dishes, too. I have included treats in the form of wholesome cakes, biscuits and snacks in the belief that these will make it easier for children to stick to a milk-exclusion diet. These have been chosen for their calcium content and also for their similarity to forbidden foods containing milk. To begin with, all trace of milk must be eliminated, which means that most shop-bought biscuits, cakes and even non-dairy ice cream are out. Eventually it may be possible to become more relaxed about the small quantities of milk in these foods, especially in cases where the allergic reaction occurs in direct proportion to the amount of allergen consumed. Ultimately children especially have a good chance of 'growing out' of a milk allergy, and this process will be aided by a wholesome, varied diet based on fresh foods in which harmful additives are kept to the minimum. As many people have more than one food allergy I have marked the recipes with symbols. Obviously all the recipes are free from cow's milk products; those marked **E** are free from eggs, and the **W** symbol denotes wheat-free recipes. Advice on which foods to buy and where to buy them can be found in chapter 2, Practical advice.

I hope this book will give encouragement to people who have been urged to persevere with a milk-exclusion diet. It's not easy at first, but it soon becomes second nature. Other family members who are not allergic can still drink milk, eat cheese etc., but all the cooking can be dairy-product free. The allergy may last for only a matter of months or a few years, so it is important to keep trying dairy products every six months or so to see if there is still an adverse reaction. Four years after starting his diet, Patrick is no longer allergic to cow's milk, and is cured of asthma, eczema and rhinitis. His body has healed itself, naturally.

TAKING CARE WHEN YOU GIVE UP MILK

According to the National Food Survey for 1986 published by the Ministry of Agriculture, Fisheries and Food (MAFF), consumption of dairy products provides 58.1 per cent of the total calcium intake in the UK diet:

Table 1: Calcium in the household diet

	mg	% of total intake
Total Ca (mg) per person per day	893	100
From dairy products	518	58.1
From cereals	218	24.5
From vegetables	58	6.5
From fish	15	1.7
From other foods	84	9.2

If cow's milk and its products are eliminated from the diet and no effort is made to consume other foods containing calcium to make up for them, then there is a danger of calcium deficiency. The purpose of this book is to make you more aware of the other dietary sources of calcium. If goat's or ewe's milk and their products are used as straight replacements for cow's milk products, then that single adaptation would be enough to balance the diet again. This is not always as easy as it sounds, since many people who are allergic to cow's milk are also allergic to goat's milk. Few people react adversely to sheep's milk products, but not everyone can readily have access to a supply of fresh or frozen ewe's milk. Soya milk, which mimics the taste of cow's milk in cooking, is low in calcium. As you can see from Table 1, cereals, vegetables (some fruit) and fish provide other sources of calcium. If replacing cow's milk with goat's or ewe's milk does not work for you, either on the grounds of allergy or difficulty concerning the supply, then it would be advisable to become more aware of these other sources of calcium, and to eat them more often.

Most of the recipes in this book are made from ingredients which contain calcium. Some recipes have been included for their vitamin D content, because vitamin D is essential in calcium absorption. These foods are also rich in other minerals and vitamins, so by eating more of them you won't become deficient in other important nutrients. However, I don't regard my selection of recipes as a diet; rather they are meant as a guide to alternative sources of calcium which can be integrated into your usual diet after you have eliminated cow's milk products. I don't imagine that all of your cooking will come out of this book, but I hope that you will become conscious of ways to include calcium-rich foods on a regular basis. Although it may appear at first as if I am being narrow by concentrating on recipes made from ingredients which contain calcium and vitamin D, it will soon become apparent that there is, in fact, a wide range of foods to choose from, to add to the large number of foods you already eat. When a major component of the diet has been eliminated, it is a good idea to eat a greater variety of foods than before, because that way your chances of restoring a balance are increased.

The importance of calcium

However advantageous it may be to eliminate milk from the diet from a food allergy point of view, the disadvantages must also be evaluated, and compensations made in order to regain a balanced diet. Dairy products are the main source of calcium in the West: a daily pint of milk on its own satisfies the current DHSS recommendations for UK calcium intake for all groups except pregnant and lactating women. Although we can obtain the minerals and vitamins present in cow's milk from a variety of foods, it is only other animal milks that supply calcium in such quantity and in such an easily absorbable form, which is bland enough to be consumed every day. Like cow's milk, human, goat's and ewe's milk are all designed to aid in the growth and development of the young. Everyone knows that calcium is essential for the formation and maintenance of strong bones and teeth. It has been estimated that 99 per cent of the calcium in the body is found in the skeleton and teeth, and 1 per cent is in the blood serum, where it performs a number of vital functions. Bone is constantly being resorbed and reformed. If the calcium in the blood is low owing to increased demand or decreased calcium absorption, then the calcium in the bone structure will be drawn upon. Growth, pregnancy and lactation all make extra claims on the calcium in the body, so a generous intake of calcium during these periods is essential. It has been suggested that strong bone formation in youth may help to prevent osteoporosis in old age. Hormonal changes affecting calcium retention in menopausal women and the decreasing ability to absorb calcium in old age in both men and women are thought to be other contributory factors to the onset of osteoporosis. Clearly, we never outgrow our need for calcium.

Calcium cannot be utilized in the body without the presence of vitamin D, which is derived from some foods and the action of sunlight on exposed skin. Vitamin D is stored in the liver and kidneys. Most people get enough from daily walks outside, when the sun acts on the skin to manufacture 'the sunshine vitamin'. Exercise itself is important for the maintenance of bone; reduction of bone mass has been observed in cases of prolonged bed rest and lengthy periods of weightlessness in space. The best food sources of vitamin D are oily fish, eggs, liver and margarine, which is fortified with vitamin D by law. Oily fish, especially those with bones, such as sardines and pilchards, are also extremely high in calcium. Aided by their own vitamin D, the calcium from these fish is readily absorbed and compensates well for the lack of cow's milk in the diet (although it is unlikely that they will be consumed every day, as milk usually is). There are a number of oily fish, egg and some liver recipes in this book.

How much calcium is necessary?

The question of how much calcium we need in order to retain balanced levels in our bodies is a complicated and controversial one. It is unrealistic to imagine that anyone can know exactly how much calcium he has absorbed in one day because of the good absorption capabilities of some foods, the chemical inhibiting factors to absorption found in certain other foods and in certain combinations of foods, as well as the varying ability to absorb the mineral among individuals. Adequate levels of vitamin D and magnesium improve absorption efficiency, while excess phosphate consumption inhibits it. Cow's, goat's and ewe's milk contain lactose, which indirectly aids calcium absorption, whereas fibre, which is often combined with phytic acid, and also oxalic acid, make calcium absorption more difficult. It has been estimated that we absorb only 20 to 30 per cent of our total calcium intake, and the rest is excreted. On the other hand, it has been contended that those who are used to a high-fibre diet can adapt and overcome much of the calcium blocking effect of fibre and phytic acid, and that those on a low-calcium intake appear to become more efficient than average in absorbing calcium.

There are no absolutes in estimating how much calcium is sufficient. It is not simply a matter of referring to a food table to gauge how many milligrams have been consumed in a day and then comparing that with the Department of Health and Social Security's *Recommended Daily Amounts of Food Energy and Nutrients for Groups of People in the United Kingdom*, of which an extract appears below (see Table 2). Firstly, the nutritional analyses found in different food table manuals do not always agree, in part reflecting the variability of foods such as cereals, fruit and vegetables according to season, soil treatment and soil structure. Secondly, there is some controversy over what levels of intake should be set. The Recommended Daily Allowances (RDAs) among Western countries disagree, as can be demonstrated by comparing the UK with the US calcium figures. In the belief that a generous calcium consumption throughout life may help to prevent the development of thin and brittle bones in old age, the National Osteoporosis Society has recently made higher recommendations, and is pressing the government to raise theirs. The UK RDAs are being reviewed at the moment by the Chief Medical Officer's Committee on the Medical Aspects of Food Policy (COMA). They are expected to make their report by September 1990. The US RDAs are also under review.

Table 2: A comparison of UK, US, and National Osteoporosis Society Recommended Daily Allowances of calcium

Category	UK	US	NOS
Young children			800mg
Children (1–8 years)	600mg	800mg	
Children (9–10 years)	700mg	800mg	
Children (11–12 years)	700mg	1,200mg	
Teenagers			1,200mg
Teenagers (13–14 years)	700mg	1,200mg	
Teenagers (15–17/18 years)	600mg	1,200mg	

Category	UK	US	NOS
Women (18/19–64 years)	500mg	800mg	
Women (20–40 years)			1,000mg
Pregnant and nursing women	1,200mg	1,200mg	1,200mg
Pregnant and nursing teenagers			1,500mg
Women over 40 (i.e., before, during and after menopause) without Hormone Replacement Therapy			1,500mg
Women over 40 with Hormone Replacement Therapy			1,000mg
Men (19–64 years)	500mg	800mg	
Men (20–60 years)			1,000mg
Men and Women over 60			1,200mg
Men and Women over 65	500mg	800mg	

The National Osteoporosis Society does not recommend anyone to have a total calcium intake of more than 2,000mg a day.

How to get enough calcium on a cow's milk-free diet

There should be no calcium deficiency in an otherwise normal diet if goat's or ewe's milk replaces cow's milk, and goat's and/or ewe's milk cheeses and yogurts replace the other dairy products. A comparison of the calcium contents of the different animal whole milks is illustrated overleaf. These are average readings from several samples. In cow's milk there is some variation in calcium, but the range of difference is not great. However it should be pointed out that the calcium content of goat's and sheep's milk varies widely according to breed, husbandry and season.

Table 3: A comparison of the calcium contents of cow's, goat's and ewe's milks

Type of milk	mg per 100g
Cow's milk	120
Goat's milk	100
Ewe's milk	180

In other respects these milks are nutritionally very similar. The fat content of ewe's milk is estimated to be about 8.5 per cent, while that of goat's milk is, on average, 4.5 per cent. Whole cow's milk is the lowest in fat, at 3.6 per cent.

Upon diagnosis of a cow's milk allergy, many people turn to soya milk without first trying goat's or sheep's milk. Although it is a useful food, soya milk should not be regarded as a replacement for cow's milk in nutritional terms. The soya milk presently on sale in the UK is not fortified, and has only on average 4 per cent of the calcium of cow's milk. Aside from calcium, the other components of goat's and ewe's milk are similar to cow's milk. Soya milk is a plant milk, made from soya beans, and is not as nutritionally rich as animal milks. However, if you do use soya milk in place of cow's milk, a good intake of goat's and/or ewe's milk cheeses and yogurts would go a long way towards maintaining former calcium levels.

Dark green leafy vegetables, wholemeal flour, wholegrains, beans, nuts, seeds, root vegetables and fruit are other sources of calcium, but they are less straightforward than, for example, animal milks or bony fish, owing to the absorption problems associated with fibre, phytic acid and oxalic acid mentioned earlier. Fibre is found in wholegrains, fruits and vegetables, and phytic acid is in certain fibrous foods: bran, nuts, seeds, wholemeals and wholegrains, peas and brown rice. Fibre and phytic acid are believed to reduce calcium absorption from both the foods themselves and other foods eaten at the same time. This does not mean that you should avoid foods which contain fibre and phytic acid. The body is still capable of absorbing a reasonable percentage of the calcium from these foods. With the exception of certain medical conditions, it should not be necessary to add uncooked bran to a diet which draws on a variety of sources of dietary fibre, such as other wholegrain products, pulses, vegetables and fruit.

Oxalic acid is found in large quantities in spinach and rhubarb. It locks much of the calcium into those foods which contain it, making it unavailable for absorption. Spinach has traditionally been regarded as a good source of calcium, partly owing to a misprint in the literature which credits it with 600mg of calcium per 100g. In fact according to the current reading from the MAFF, cooked spinach has 150mg of calcium per 100g. A recent study on human subjects demonstrated that on average only 5% of the calcium from spinach was absorbed (Heaney, R.P., Weaver, C.M., and Recker, R.R., [1988] Calcium absorbability from spinach, *Am. J. Clin. Nutr.* 47 [4], 707–709). However spinach is still a useful source of vitamins, and I have included two recipes using it in conjunction with calcium-rich ingredients.

Bread is an important source of calcium in the diet. The practice of fortifying white flour with calcium carbonate, iron, vitamin B_1 and niacin began in the UK during the Second World War, in order to make up for the nutrients lost in the milling process. This enrichment of white but not wholemeal flour is still required by law, even though it is not necessary to state it on flour and bread labels. As a result of supplementation, white bread and breads other than wholemeal tend to be higher in calcium than wholemeal bread. The most recently published data on the calcium analyses of bread can be found in Table 6 on page 22. These readings have been adapted from B. Holland, I.D. Unwin and D.H. Buss's *Cereal and Cereal Products, Third Supplement to McCance and Widdowson's The Composition of Foods*, The Royal Society of Chemistry and MAFF, HMSO, 1988. However the information directly from the food industry is that levels of calcium in bread, especially in wholemeal bread, are now much higher. During the last year or two it has become common practice for extra calcium to be added to the flour as one of the components of breadmaking. For example British Bakeries gave the following

estimates: wholemeal, 90–100mg per 100g; white, up to 150mg; softgrain, 150–160mg per 100g (a 100g serving is roughly equivalent to 2–2 ½ slices). Bread from the major national bakeries, supermarket bakeries and small independent bakeries all have levels of calcium similar to these estimates in the range of breads they offer.

There is more fibre in wholemeal bread than in white bread, but much of the phytic acid is broken down by a yeast enzyme during the course of the bread making. Wholemeal bread is still a good source of calcium, and anyone who enjoys eating it should carry on. On a milk-free diet it would be worthwhile also eating some of the breads made from white flour or a mix including white flour, such as some granary breads and brown breads. All bread contains calcium, but each type has slightly different nutritional qualities, textures and tastes, so choosing a variety of breads is a good idea. Bread is a body-building food for growing children, and is especially important for teenagers, who seem to crave it. Putting bread on the table at every meal is a good way to raise the family's calcium intake.

For baking, plain white flour has more calcium than wholemeal flour, but both white and wholemeal self-raising flour now often have bicarbonate of soda and acid calcium phosphate as raising agents. Recipes using self-raising flour or baking powder can be very good sources of dietary calcium. The recipes in this book do not stipulate which sort of flour to use, other than plain or self-raising, so it is up to the reader to choose white, wholemeal or other on the basis of information from this chapter, and according to the allergy and calcium requirements of each individual case. You may wish to experiment with white and wholemeal flour in the cakes, biscuits and pastry, to see which you prefer. I have used black strap molasses and Muscovado sugar in a number of cake and biscuit recipes because these pure cane sugar products are high in calcium. The taste of Muscovado is stronger than white sugar, so less of it is needed in a recipe to make cakes and biscuits moist and full of flavour. Black treacle, which is usually made from a combination of sugar beet and cane syrups, is a good source of calcium, but pure cane molasses is better (compare the calcium reading of each in Table 11 on page 24).

The calcium absorption from nuts and seeds is to a certain extent affected by the presence of phytic acid. Since the phytic acid is largely in the outer casings of plant matter, it is useful to know that blanched and ground almonds without their skins contain less phytic acid, and this is also true of other skinned nuts. Almonds are extremely high in calcium, containing twice as much calcium as milk, although weight for weight it is easier to consume 100g of milk than 100g of almonds. Sesame seeds are also considered to be a good source of calcium, as is the paste made from them, tahini.

The best cow's milk-free sources of calcium

By now it should be obvious how difficult it is to assess precisely how much calcium we can absorb from different foods and how much calcium we should be aiming to consume in the first place. In the end, a common sense approach is the best one. The range of RDAs from UK to US to National Osteoporosis Society could be viewed as a more than adequate to optimum guide. By referring to the table below you should be able to estimate roughly if you can get a sufficient calcium intake from a cow's milk-free diet by eating more of the other calcium-rich foods. This does not mean eating more; it is really a matter of choosing to eat high-calcium foods on a regular basis. The foods in the following tables are the ones most often used in the recipes. The calcium levels have been taken mostly from published sources and are rounded up or down to the nearest 5 milligrams.

Table 4: Cow's milk alternatives

Best sources of calcium	Approximate mg per 100g	Best sources of calcium	Approximate mg per 100g
blue sheep's milk cheese (Roquefort)	520	sheep's milk Feta cheese	430
hard sheep's milk cheese	—	soft goat's milk cheese	—
hard goat's milk cheese	—	goat's milk yogurt	120
Greek and Pure sheep's milk yogurt	119	sheep's milk	180
goat's milk Feta cheese	330	goat's milk	100
		unfortified soya milk	5

Table 5: Fish

Best sources of calcium	Approximate mg per 100g	Best sources of calcium	Approximate mg per 100g
whitebait, fried	860	haddock, fried; scampi, fried in breadcrumbs	100
sprats, fried	620	salmon, canned; clams, canned; plaice, fried in breadcrumbs; fish cakes, fried	75
sardines, canned in oil, fish only	550	kipper, baked; smoked haddock, steamed	60
sardines, canned in tomato sauce	460	fish fingers, fried; plaice, steamed	45
shrimps, boiled; fish paste; pilchards, canned in tomato sauce; anchovies	300	crab, boiled; cod fillet, poached; salmon, steamed	30
mussels, boiled; oysters, raw; clams, boiled	200	cod fillet, baked; lemon sole, steamed	25
prawns boiled, without shells	150	salmon, smoked	20
cockles, boiled	130		
bloaters, grilled; scallops; crab, canned	120		

A line indicates that the figures are unavailable.

The calcium levels of canned fish are high partly because the readings include all bones, many of which are often discarded before consumption. The bones should be mashed up and eaten with the fish in order not to waste a good source of calcium.

Table 6: Cereals

Best sources of calcium	Approximate mg per 100g	Best sources of calcium	Approximate mg per 100g
Flour		baby rusks	520–610
self-raising white	350	fruit scones, from a bakery	150
plain white	140	water biscuits	140
brown	130	ginger nut biscuits	
wholemeal	40	semi-sweet biscuits	
Bread and rolls:		Swiss-style muesli	130
Vitbe	150	crumpets, toasted	
white rolls, crusty	140	cream crackers	110
French stick	130	cooked pastry made with white flour	
breadcrumbs, homemade		teacakes, toasted	100
wheatgerm bread		plain chocolate digestive biscuits	90
Hovis bread	120	Special K	70
white rolls, soft		Ready Brek	65
hamburger buns	110	raw oatmeal or porridge oats	55
brown bread		cooked wholemeal pastry	30
brown rolls	100		
granary bread	75		
wholemeal rolls			
wholemeal bread	55		
Biscuits, buns and cereals:			
baby cereals	710–870		

Table 7: Beans

Best sources of calcium	Approximate mg per 100g	Best sources of calcium	Approximate mg per 100g
tofu (soya bean curd)	500	baked beans, canned	45
TVP mince, made up or canned	80	French beans, boiled	40
		mung beans (dahl), cooked	35
haricot beans, cooked soya beans, cooked chick peas, cooked	65	runner beans, cooked	25
		broad beans, cooked	20
kidney beans, cooked	50		

Table 8: Vegetables

Best sources of calcium	Approximate mg per 100g	Best sources of calcium	Approximate mg per 100g
parsley, raw	330	white cabbage, raw radishes	45
watercress, raw	220		
Chinese leaves, raw	150	carrots, boiled winter cabbage, boiled swede, boiled parsnips, boiled potato crisps	40
spring onions	140		
broccoli tops, raw	100		
broccoli tops, cooked	80		
Savoy cabbage, raw	75		
mustard and cress	70	beetroot, boiled courgettes, boiled onions, raw Jerusalem artichokes, boiled	30
onions, fried leeks, boiled turnips, boiled winter cabbage, raw	60		
		Brussels sprouts, boiled	25
celery, raw or boiled olives, pickled Savoy cabbage, boiled carrots, raw	50	avocado	15

Table 9: Nuts and seeds

Best sources of calcium	Approximate mg per 100g	Best sources of calcium	Approximate mg per 100g
almonds	250	walnuts	
Brazil nuts	180	peanuts	60
Barcelona nuts	170	chestnuts	
tahini		hazel-nuts	45
sesame seeds	130	pumpkin seeds	
sunflower seeds	120	cashew nuts	
		peanut butter	35

Table 10: Fruit

Best sources of calcium	Approximate mg per 100g	Best sources of calcium	Approximate mg per 100g
figs, dried	280	oranges, peeled	
currants, dried	95	tangerines	
apricots, dried	90	redcurrants	40
dates, dried	70	blackberries, stewed with sugar	
raisins, dried		gooseberries, stewed with sugar	20
blackcurrants	60	white grapes	
blackberries			
sultanas, dried	50		

Table 11: Miscellaneous

Best sources of calcium	Approximate mg per 100g	Best sources of calcium	Approximate mg per 100g
baking powder	1,130	cocoa powder	130
black strap molasses	640	Muscovado sugar	92
black treacle	500	eggs	52
carob powder (Kalibu)	225		

Remember that 100g equals about 3½ oz, and that a number of the items in the above tables would normally be consumed in very small amounts. For example, parsley is high in calcium, 330mg per 100g, but 3½ oz of parsley is about seven times as much as would be called for in a recipe serving four to six people. On the other hand, 3½ oz of Greek and Pure sheep's milk yogurt is a realistic portion, containing on average 119mg of calcium, or one fifth of the RDA for children.

In addition to these foods, it should not be forgotten that water, especially hard water, can be a valuable source of calcium. A phone call to the regional water authority chemist will enable you to determine if the local water supply is soft, average, or hard, and to estimate how much calcium you are adding to your diet from drinking water.

Calcium supplementation

Although it is preferable to get all the necessary vitamins and minerals directly from the diet, there are medical conditions for which calcium supplementation is prescribed. The small doses found in multi-vitamin and mineral tablets are safe, but no one should take a larger dose than 100mg without medical advice. The body will tend to excrete excess calcium, but a long-term supplement, especially when taken with extra vitamin D, can lead to the formation of calcium deposits in the kidneys, heart and other soft tissues. This can happen inadvertently by buying high-dose calcium pills, perhaps with added vitamin D to facilitate absorption, then supplementing these with cod liver oil capsules (containing more vitamin D) at the onset of winter, and repeating this annually for as long as the milk allergy lasts, which may be several years or indefinitely. Children and teenagers, pregnant, lactating and post-menopausal women, men and women over 60 and osteoporosis sufferers should be particularly careful about getting enough calcium on a milk-free diet. Any doubts should be discussed with a member of the medical profession. If you have a history of kidney stones you should consult your doctor about desirable calcium levels, as supplementation could be dangerous.

PRACTICAL ADVICE

1 Margarines

When a milk allergy is first diagnosed, all trace of cow's milk must be eliminated from the diet. Some people react violently to minute amounts of cow's milk, so in order to give the new milk-free diet a chance even the small amounts of whey, lactose, casein and caseinates in prepared foods should be avoided. Whey is used in the manufacture of most vegetable margarines, but there are a number of pure vegetable margarines and spreads which are available in health food shops and supermarkets. The recipes in this book do not specify which margarine to use, but it is assumed that it will be a milk-free one.

2 Goat's milk

Many people who have not tried it dislike the idea of goat's milk on the grounds that it tastes strong. A good supplier will not feed the goats on strong tasting foods, such as brassicas, and will handle the fresh or frozen milk quickly and hygienically, so that the milk does not begin to turn sour before it is purchased. Well-produced goat's milk should taste like cow's milk. It is palatable on its own as a beverage, in hot drinks, and in both sweet and savoury cooking. Finding a good supplier is essential. Small-scale producers do not pasteurize goat's milk, and therefore great care must be paid to hygiene. Pasteurization of goat's (and also sheep's) milk is not required by law, and consequently without this heat treatment there is a slight danger of bacterial contamination. Babies should not be given goat's milk which has not been diluted and boiled first, and then only on the advice of a doctor. Goat's milk can usually be kept for up to four days in the refrigerator, but as with cow's milk, any goat's milk that smells sour should be thrown out. The British Goat Society have set very high standards of hygiene for their members. They would be able to give you information about goat's milk producers in your area if you write to them at 34/36 Fore Street, Bovey Tracey, Newton Abbot, Devon, TQ13 9AD. Their telephone number is 0626 833168.

If you are able to locate a good supplier of goat's milk nearby, the farmer may deliver fresh and frozen goat's milk to your house, perhaps once a week. The availability of unpasteurized goat's milk can be a problem, especially in the winter when it is natural for the pregnant goats to stop lactating. Some herds are made to kid in rotation to overcome this difficulty. A back-up supply of dried or UHT goat's milk might help.

Health food shops sell goat's milk in many forms, e.g., unpasteurized frozen, pasteurized fresh, UHT or dried. Many of the larger supermarkets sell pasteurized fresh or UHT goat's milk. If your local supermarket does not stock either of these products, you could ask the manager or phone their head office and request that they do. It would be a good idea to look into all the alternatives to see if any of these forms of goat's milk suits you.

3 Ewe's (sheep's) milk

You may want to investigate ewe's milk before trying goat's milk, or you may turn to it if goat's milk causes an allergic reaction. Sheep's milk is creamy and pleasant tasting, and is produced in much the same way as goat's milk. However at present it is not as widely available as goat's milk. Sheep's milk is not sold in supermarkets, but many health food shops sell sheep's milk products. There are increasing numbers of

farmers who produce and sell unpasteurized fresh and frozen ewe's milk, and ewe's milk yogurt and cheese. The best way to start is by finding out where your nearest suppliers are. This information can be obtained from the British Sheep Dairying Association, Wield Wood, Alresford, Hampshire SO24 9RU. Their telephone number is 0420 63151.

4 Goat's and ewe's milk cheeses

Feta cheese is the cheapest and best alternative to Cheddar and Mozzarella for cooking. It can be made either from ewe's milk or goat's milk, but there is also a cow's milk version, so be sure to check. In order for Feta to melt properly in cooking it has to be grated finely in a hand-held grater. Sometimes Feta is very salty, in which case no other salt needs to be added to savoury recipes. Some of the hard goat's and

sheep's milk cheeses can be finely grated and used in place of Parmesan cheese, for example, Ribblesdale, of which there are both goat's and ewe's milk varieties and also the ewe's milk Dudleswell. Like many of the ewe's milk cheeses, Roquefort is expensive, but it is marvellous in cooking, where a little bit goes a long way.

Larger supermarkets sell ewe's milk Feta, and

also Chèvre, the soft, white goat's cheese, or sometimes a similar goat's cheese, Cabrette. Other goat's and ewe's milk cheeses can be found in speciality cheese shops and delicatessens, where you are likely to find Roquefort and Feta. Some goat's cheeses you may wish to try are Glencoe, a full-fat soft cheese from Scotland; Capricorn, a Brie-type cheese from Somerset; and Allerdale, Thixendale and Robrock, which are Cheddar-like cheeses. Among the best sheep cheeses are Acorn, Cecilia, Carolina, Sheviock, Bronte Country, Colford Blue and Lanark Blue. Many of these cheeses are available by mail order, so it would be worth asking the British Goat Society or the British Sheep Dairying Association for information on them.

5 Goat's and ewe's milk yogurts

Both goat's and ewe's milk plain yogurts can be used in place of cream and sour cream in cooking, with fruit and as a topping for desserts. British goat's and sheep's milk yogurts are sold directly by the producers, in health food shops, or in the case of goat's milk yogurt, in some supermarkets. Pure fruit yogurts are also produced.

It should be noted that not all Greek sheep's milk yogurt is made exclusively from sheep's milk. One of the most popular brands has added cow's cream. The most widely distributed 100 per cent ewe's milk Greek yogurt is Greek and Pure Ewe's Milk Yogurt (Quality Foods Limited, London) which is sold in some of the larger supermarkets as well as in a number of healthfood shops and delicatessens. This thick and creamy yogurt is 6 per cent fat, so it is not as low in fat as cow's milk low-fat yogurts, which are slightly over 1 per cent, but it compares well with low-fat fromage frais (about 8 per cent). To complete the comparison, double cream is 48 per cent fat. Greek and Pure Ewe's Milk Yogurt is made from pasteurized milk.

6 Soya milk

It cannot be stressed enough that unfortified soya milk has, on average, only 4 per cent of the calcium of cow's milk and it must not be regarded as its nutritional equivalent. However, it is possible that a supplier of long-life soya milk will soon produce a line that is fortified with calcium. There has been a fresh fortified soya milk which was withdrawn from sale.

When goat's milk cannot be tolerated and when ewe's milk is difficult to get, soya milk is a useful alternative. Again, some people are allergic to soya protein, so be careful when introducing soya milk, soya beans, tofu and textured vegetable protein (TVP). Soya milk is very convenient to buy from health food shops and larger supermarkets, and comes in sweetened and unsweetened forms. The tastes vary, so it is worth trying out different brands. Only the unsweetened variety is suitable for cooking savoury dishes, and it can also be used on cereal and in hot drinks, although those with a sweet tooth tend to prefer sweetened soya milk for these purposes.

7 Lactose-reduced milk

Lactose-reduced milk has been developed for people with a lactose intolerance. This condition is caused by an inability of the stomach to produce lactase, which is necessary for breaking down the lactose in milk. It must be emphasized that goat's and sheep's milk also contain lactose. People who suffer from lactose intolerance may find they can digest lactose-reduced cow's milk. Lactaid, produced by MyPlan of Halifax is a low-fat milk to which lactase has been added. It is available from chemists, health food shops, and some supermarkets. Lactolite, produced by Associated Fresh Foods, is another lactose-reduced milk which has a standard fat content and is therefore more suitable for babies and young children, who should not be given low-fat milk. Alternatively, there are lactase drops, which can be added to ordinary cow's milk. Hard cheese such as Cheddar and cow's milk yogurt may also be tolerated because of their low lactose level. A doctor or chemist would be able to give further advice.

8 Cooking methods

It should be pointed out that the recipes in this book are based on a teaspoon equalling 6ml, not 5ml, a dessertspoon equalling 12ml, not 10ml, and a tablespoon equalling 18ml, not 15ml. These are clearly marked in the text. Where neither sweetened nor unsweetened soya milk is specified, either will do.

Another thing that you should be aware of is that cooking in water and steaming have an effect on the calcium levels of food. Long cooking times allow significant amounts of calcium to leach out of the food into the water. For example, according to figures supplied by the Institute of Food Research in Norwich, Brussels sprouts will lose about 25 per cent of their calcium when boiled for 20–30 minutes. However, this leaching is minimal using short cooking times. If the cooking water is saved and used as stock for gravy or soup, then none of the leached calcium will be wasted; it is only lost if the water is thrown away. It is a good idea to freeze the water that vegetables have been cooked in if you have no immediate need for it, so that you can use it later for stock. The ingredients in soups and casseroles are not subject to leaching of calcium because the calcium will be retained in the broth. Dried beans must be cooked for a long time, but fresh vegetables taste better and are better for you if they are cooked as quickly as possible, using the minimum amount of water. Food cooked in a microwave oven retains vitamins and minerals better than the other cooking methods. Although the recipes in this book are not written with microwave instructions, if you have one you could use it to cook some of the ingredients, such as vegetables.

The best way to eat vegetables is in their raw state, and salads should be a regular part of everyone's diet. In order to keep those you are feeding healthy, the ideal is to serve one salad meal and one cooked meal daily with a variety of vegetables and plenty of fresh fruit, although this may not always be possible (ideas for packed lunches can be found on page 156). Don't despair if there is no time to cook: baked beans on toast is a well-balanced meal, an excellent source of calcium *and* can be put on the table in a flash!

Sources
Table 1: National Food Survey for 1986, MAFF, adapted material.
Table 2: DHSS, 'Report on Health and Social Subjects 15', *Recommended Daily Amounts of Food Energy and Nutrients for Groups of People in the United Kingdom*, COMA, HMSO, 1979, adapted material (Crown copyright material is adapted with the permission of the Controller of Her Majesty's Stationery Office); *Recommended Dietary Allowances*, Committee on Dietary Allowances, Food and Nutrition Board, Division of Biological Sciences, Assembly of Life Sciences, National Research Council, National Academy of Sciences, Washington, DC, 1980, adapted material; Recommended Daily Allowances of Calcium, National Osteoporosis Society, figures for 1988.
Table 3: MAFF.
Tables 4–11: A.E. Bender and D.A. Bender, *Food Tables*, OUP, 1986, adapted material; 'Bundesministerium für Ernährung, Landwirtschaft und Forsten', Bonn, Food Composition and Nutrition Tables, 1986–87 (ewe's milk Feta reading); MAFF; A.A. Paul and D.A.T. Southgate, *McCance and Widdowson's The Composition of Foods*, MAFF, HMSO, 1985, adapted material; I.D. Unwin and D.H. Buss, *Cereals and Cereal Products* (Supplement to *McCance and Widdowson's The Composition of Foods*), MAFF, HMSO, 1988, adapted material (Crown copyright material is adapted with the permission of the Controller of Her Majesty's Stationery Office); Isabel Skypala, *Healthy Eating*, Wisebuy Publications, London, 1988, adapted material; calcium levels of brand-named items from producers.

APPETIZERS

DIPS

The following dips, based on ewe's or goat's milk yogurt, are fast and easy to make. Serve them with raw broccoli florets, celery, carrots or crisps for wholesome and delicious hors d'oeuvres. They are filling enough for a grown-up's lunch or an after-school snack for children.

Yogurt and Chive Dip _____ W

Serves 6

If you like a strong garlic flavour, infuse the garlic clove in the lemon juice for an hour or two before making the dip. Fresh chives are hard to come by in winter, but if you grow them in the garden in the summer you can freeze them easily. Just wash and chop them, put them in a plastic container and freeze.

2 teaspoons (12ml) lemon juice
1 garlic clove
2 tablespoons (36ml) chopped fresh chives
8 tablespoons (144ml) sheep's or goat's milk yogurt
2 tablespoons (18ml) mayonnaise

1. Put the lemon juice in an egg cup, then crush the garlic clove and add it to the lemon juice.
2. Mix the chives in a bowl with the yogurt and mayonnaise.
3. Discard the garlic clove and stir the lemon juice into the yogurt and mayonnaise mixture.
4. Chill the dip for a couple of hours to allow the flavours to develop and serve with sliced raw vegetables.

Guacamole _____ E W

Serves 4

The onion, garlic, and green pepper can be sautéed in oil first in order to make them more digestible.

1 average ripe avocado, peeled
1 tablespoon (18ml) tomato purée
1 tablespoon (18ml) onion, finely chopped
1 clove garlic, minced
1 tablespoon (18ml) green pepper, finely chopped
1 tablespoon (18ml) lemon juice
¼ teaspoon (1ml) Tabasco sauce
¼ pint (140ml) sheep's or goat's milk yogurt

1. Mash or liquidize all the ingredients.
2. Serve as a dip for raw vegetables, corn chips, or as an accompaniment to chilli.

Avocado Dip _____ E W

Serves 3

This is light and refreshing, and a delightful pale green in colour. It tastes strongly of avocado, and is quite different from the spicier Guacamole.

1 ripe avocado, about 6 oz (170g)
1 teaspoon (6ml) lemon juice
3 tablespoons (54ml) sheep's or goat's milk yogurt

1. Peel and stone the avocado and put it in a flat-bottomed bowl.
2. Sprinkle the lemon juice over the avocado and mash roughly.
3. Add the yogurt and continue mashing until smooth.
4. Serve with slivered raw vegetables or tortilla chips.

Humus _____ E   W

Serves 6

4 oz (115g) chick peas, soaked overnight,
  or 10oz (285g) cooked
4 oz (115g) sheep's or goat's milk yogurt
1 garlic clove, crushed
1 tablespoon (18ml) olive oil

1. Rinse the chick peas and boil them for
   about 1½ hours or until soft.
   Alternatively, drain 10 oz (285g) chick
   peas from a tin.
2. Put the chick peas in a handgrater or a
   food processor fitted with the metal
   blade.
3. Add the yogurt to the chick peas along
   with the crushed garlic clove and olive
   oil.
4. Purée the mixture until smooth.
5. Serve with broccoli florets, strips of red
   or green pepper, carrot and celery
   sticks, etc.

Garlic and Herb Spread_____ E   W

Serves 6

For a strong garlic taste, use two garlic cloves and make the spread ahead of time in order
for the flavours to develop. This looks and tastes like similar spreads made from cream cheese.

8 oz (225g) tofu
2 tablespoons sheep's or goat's milk yogurt
2 tablespoons (36ml) fresh parsley,
  chopped
2 tablespoons fresh chives, chopped
1 or 2 garlic cloves, minced
2 spring onions, chopped

1. Drain the tofu and put it in a food
   processor fitted with the metal blade.
2. Add the other ingredients and mix until
   smooth.
3. Serve with sesame biscuits or slivered
   raw vegetables.

Roquefort Dip

Serves 6

8 oz (225g) tub sheep's or goat's milk
yogurt

2 oz (55g) Roquefort or Lanark Blue
cheese

½ teaspoon (3ml) onion, grated

1 dessertspoon (12ml) fresh parsley,
chopped

1. In a flat-bottomed bowl, mix the
   yogurt, cheese and onion together with
   a potato masher.
2. Put the dip in a small bowl and top
   with parsley.
3. Serve with slivered courgettes, carrots,
   celery, broccoli and cauliflower florets
   or crisps.

PÂTÉS AND MOUSSES

Sardine Pâté _____ E W

Serves 4

4⅓ oz (125g) tin sardines in oil
2 oz (55g) Feta cheese, finely grated
1 tablespoon (18ml) concentrated tomato
  purée
1 dessertspoon (12ml) lemon juice
2 tablespoons (36ml) sheep's or goat's milk
  yogurt

1. Drain the sardines, then mix in all the other ingredients with a potato masher in a flat-bottomed bowl.
2. Serve on toast as a starter, or use as a sandwich filling.

Kipper Pâté _____ E W

Serves 4 or 8

Try to get naturally smoked, undyed kippers. This recipe can be made with bloaters rather than kippers.

2 kipper fillets
3 oz (85g) soft margarine
6 tablespoons (108ml) sheep's or goat's
  milk yogurt
1 teaspoon (6ml) lemon juice

1. Cover the kippers with boiling water and leave them for 10 minutes.
2. Skin the kippers and remove any large bones, then chop them roughly.
3. Mash or liquidize the fish with the other ingredients.
4. Put the pâté in 4 ramekins or 8 egg cups and serve with toast fingers.

Pilchard and Tomato Spread _____ E

Serves 4 to 5

This is a good recipe for people who say they don't like pilchards, because of its mild taste. In fact my family thought it was tuna salad the first time I served it to them in sandwiches. Both the pilchard and tomato spread and the sardine pâté are very quick to make for lunch and are extremely economical.

5½ oz (155g) tin pilchards in tomato sauce
½ slice white bread
2 tablespoons (36ml) sheep's or goat's milk
   yogurt

1. Combine all the ingredients to make a smooth paste. Either grate the bread and mash it into the sardines and yogurt, or whizz it all in a food processor fitted with the metal blade.
2. Serve on toast or use as a sandwich filling.

Smoked Salmon Pâté _____ E W

Serves 4 or 8

This pâté is very filling, and when served in ramekins could be a light lunch, with a side salad. As a starter it could be put in egg cups with toast fingers at the side, in which case there would be eight portions.

8 oz (225g) smoked salmon trimmings
2oz (55g) soft margarine
3 tablespoons (54ml) sheep's or goat's milk
   yogurt
½ teaspoon lemon juice
4 slices cucumber

1. Combine all the ingredients and liquidize until smooth.
2. Put into 4 ramekins and garnish with cucumber twists.
3. Serve with toast, without margarine.

Chicken Liver Pâté

Serves 6

This pâté has a sophisticated taste and is a good first course for a dinner party.

1 lb (445g) chicken livers
2 tablespoons (36ml) flour
Sea salt and freshly ground black pepper
2 cloves garlic, finely chopped
A little bacon fat
4 oz (115g) mushrooms, sliced
4 fl oz (120ml) white wine

1. Rinse the chicken livers, trim and chop them roughly, then dredge in seasoned flour.
2. Melt the garlic in a little bacon fat, then add the chicken livers and cook them for 5 minutes, turning frequently.
3. Add the mushrooms and cook them until soft.
4. Turn the liver mixture into a food processor fitted with the metal blade, or a handgrater.
5. Purée while adding the wine slowly, until the pâté is very smooth. It will seem too wet at this stage, but it will firm up when chilled.
6. Pour into 6 ramekins, chill, then serve with toast triangles.

Everyday Liver Pâté

Serves 4

This is a nutritious and economical pâté for family lunches or teas. It is fiddly to make, so it's a good idea to double the recipe and freeze half.

½ lb (225g) pig's liver
Water
1 dessertspoon (12ml) wine vinegar
½ clove garlic, minced
1 small eating apple, peeled and diced
1 small onion, chopped roughly
1 oz (30g) margarine
1 oz (30g) flour
¼ pint (140ml) goat's or sheep's milk or unsweetened soya milk
1 egg
Sea salt and freshly ground black pepper
1 bay leaf

1. Cover the liver with the water to which the vinegar has been added, and leave overnight.
2. Pre-heat the oven to 275°F/140°C (Gas Mark 1). Grease a 1½ pint (850ml) pie dish lightly with margarine.
3. In a food processor fitted with the metal blade, chop the garlic, apple and onion.
4. Roughly chop the liver and add it to the other ingredients in the food processor. Purée until smooth.
5. Make a thick white sauce by melting the margarine, stirring in the flour and then the the goat's or soya milk. Pour it into the food processor bowl.
6. Crack the egg and add it, with seasoning, to the liver mixture.
7. Mix until smooth, then turn into the greased pie dish. Top with the bay leaf and cover with an oval of lightly greased greaseproof paper.
8. Place the dish in a roasting tin full of water and cook for about 1¾ hours, or until firm and brown in colour.
9. Remove from the oven and cool. *Freeze at this point if desired.*
10. Serve with toast or use as a sandwich filling.

EGGS AND CHEESE
Devilled Eggs _____ W

Serves 3

3 eggs, hard-boiled
½ teaspoon (3ml) French mustard
½ teaspoon (3ml) curry powder
1 tablespoon (18ml) goat's or sheep's milk
  yogurt
1 tablespoon (18ml) mayonnaise
½ teaspoon (3ml) onion, grated
Sea salt and freshly grated black pepper
1 dessertspoon (12ml) fresh parsley,
  chopped

1. Cut the hard-boiled eggs in half and put the yolks in a flat-bottomed bowl.
2. Add the mustard, curry powder, yogurt, mayonnaise, onion and seasoning to the yolks and mash thoroughly with a potato masher until smooth.
3. Stuff the egg whites with the yolk mixture, and sprinkle the chopped parsley on top.
4. Serve as hors d'oeuvre or as an accompaniment to salads.

Roquefort Rarebit Spread _____ E W

Serves 4

1 oz (30g) Roquefort cheese
3 oz (85g) Feta cheese
1 oz (30g) soft margarine
2 tablespoons (36ml) sheep's or goat's milk
  yogurt
1 tablespoon (18ml) cider (optional)
4 celery sticks or 4 slices bread

1. In a shallow bowl with a wide bottom, mash the two cheeses, soft margarine and yogurt, with a potato masher.
2. Stir in the cider, if desired.
3. Use immediately, or put the spread into a crock and chill for a few hours in order to let the flavours develop further.
4. Serve as a stuffing for celery. Alternatively use in place of cheese as cheese on toast: toast the bread lightly, then put the spread on the untoasted side and brown under the grill.

Cheese Straws

Makes 50

These are useful as a savoury snack for children. They keep well in a tin, but will probably disappear fast.

4 oz (115g) flour
Pinch of salt
1 teaspoon (6ml) dry English mustard
   powder
2 oz (55g) margarine
3 oz (85g) Feta cheese, finely grated
1 egg yolk, beaten

1. Pre-heat the oven to 375°F/190°C (Gas Mark 5), and grease two baking trays.
2. Sift together the flour, salt and mustard, and rub in the margarine.
3. Add the cheese and mix it in with the beaten egg yolk.
4. Roll out very thinly on a floured surface, and cut into about 50 fingers.
5. Bake for 15–20 minutes, or until crisp and golden.

Cheese and Garlic Stuffed Mushrooms_____

Serves 6

The amount of garlic in this recipe can be reduced according to taste.

3 cloves garlic, minced
2 tablespoons (36ml) olive oil
1 lb (455g) large, flat mushrooms (should be 12 mushrooms)
2 oz (55g) dried breadcrumbs
2 oz (55g) Feta cheese
1 dessertspoon (12ml) fresh parsley, chopped
1 egg, beaten
Sea salt and freshly ground black pepper
Few watercress leaves

1. Pre-heat the oven to 350°F/180°C (Gas Mark 4).
2. In a small non-stick frying pan, sauté the garlic in the olive oil.
3. Wash and wipe the mushrooms and cut off the stalks. Chop the stalks finely and add them to the garlic and olive oil.
4. Put the breadcrumbs, cheese, parsley, egg and seasoning in a bowl. Stir in the garlic, olive oil and mushroom stalks.
5. Stuff the mushrooms with the mixture, place them on a grill rack, and bake for 15–20 minutes. Serve two mushrooms per person, garnished with watercress.

Pink Eggs and Shrimp Salad _____W

Serves 4

This is a pretty appetizer, quick to make and not too filling.

2 eggs
4 oz (115 g) shredded lettuce
4 tablespoons (72ml) Russian dressing (see page 123)
Salt and freshly ground black pepper
4 oz (115g) cooked shrimps

1. Hard boil the eggs for 10 minutes, run them under the cold tap, peel and cool.
2. In each of 4 ramekins, layer ¼ of the Russian dressing. Season.
3. Top each portion with shrimps and serve.

SOUPS

Homemade soup is delicious, nutritious and versatile. It can be served either as a first course, or for lunch with bread and cheese or a sandwich. It is still possible to have creamed soups on a milk-free diet, using goat's, ewe's or soya milk with potato as the thickener, or a dollop of ewe's or goat's milk yogurt in place of cream. A spoonful of fresh chopped parsley or a sprig of watercress add extra calcium. Hot soup is useful as a winter warmer, but chilled soups can be refreshing in the summer, too.

The hot soups in this chapter can be frozen at the stage immediately before serving. If you are using goat's milk or ewe's milk which has been frozen in any of the appropriate recipes, freeze the soup at the vegetable purée stage, thaw, then stir in the defrosted milk before re-heating.

Borscht _____ E W

Serves 6

½ lb (225g) raw beetroot, scrubbed and
  sliced
1 carrot, scrubbed and sliced
1 onion, chopped
1 clove garlic, minced
2 tablespoons (36ml) concentrated tomato
  purée
2 pints (1.1 litres) stock made from
  2 teaspoons (12ml) yeast extract
Sea salt and freshly ground black pepper
6 tablespoons (108ml) or more of sheep's
  or goat's milk yogurt

1. Put the prepared beetroot, carrot,
   onion and garlic in a large saucepan
   with the tomato purée.
2. Add half the stock, bring to the boil
   and simmer until all the vegetables are
   tender.
3. Purée the vegetables and stock in a
   food processor or handgrater.
4. Return the soup to the saucepan and
   stir in the rest of the stock. Season.
5. Heat and serve with a dollop of yogurt
   on each portion.

Fennel Soup _____ E W

Serves 4

·This soup is delicious with croûtons. Allow ½ slice of bread per person. Cut the bread into
cubes and sauté them in olive oil. If you have made them ahead of time, crisp the croûtons
in the oven before serving.

½ lb (225g) bulb fennel, trimmed and
  chopped
½ onion, chopped
10 oz (285g) potatoes, peeled and sliced
1 pint (570ml) chicken stock, made from a
  stock cube
½ pint (285ml) goat's or sheep's milk or
  unsweetened soya milk
Sea salt and freshly ground black pepper

1. Prepare the vegetables, reserving the
   fennel leaves for garnish.
2. Put the vegetables in a large saucepan
   with the chicken stock. Bring them to
   the boil and simmer until tender.
3. Sieve or purée the soup in a
   handgrater, frozen processor, or
   liquidizer.
4. Pour the purée back into the saucepan,
   and stir in the milk. Season.
5. Heat and serve the soup, with a few
   chopped fennel leaves on each portion.

Carrot and Lentil Soup _____ E W

Serves 4

This is a good soup for people who like plain, wholesome food.

1 onion, chopped
1 dessertspoon (12ml) oil
1 lb (455g) carrots
2 pints (1.1 litres) chicken stock, made
  from 2 stock cubes
4 oz (115g) no-soak lentils
Sea salt and freshly ground black pepper
Chopped fresh parsley

1. Melt the onion in the oil in a large non-stick frying pan.
2. Scrub and slice the carrots and add them to the onions. Cook for 5 minutes, tossing frequently.
3. Add 1½ pints (850ml) chicken stock and the lentils to the pan and cook on a low heat for 1 hour.
4. Sieve by hand, or purée in a food processor or liquidizer, half at a time.
5. Pour the carrot and lentil mixture into a saucepan and add the other ½ pint (285ml) chicken stock. Add more water if the soup seems too thick.
6. Heat, season to taste and serve with some chopped fresh parsley on each portion.

Cream of Broccoli Soup _____ E W

Serves 4

½ lb (225g) broccoli or calabrese
½ medium onion, chopped
1 medium potato, peeled and sliced
Sea salt and freshly ground black pepper
1½ pints (850ml) chicken stock, made with
  a stock cube
19 fl oz (500ml) goat's milk or sheep's
  milk or unsweetened soya milk
4 tablespoons (72ml) or more of sheep's or
  goat's milk yogurt

1. Wash the broccoli, then trim off the leaves and rough stalks. Cut the broccoli head into small florets, and the stem into strips.
2. Put the broccoli in a large saucepan, then add the onion, potatoes, seasonings and stock.
3. Bring the vegetables to the boil, then simmer for 20 minutes.
4. Purée the soup in a handgrater or food

processor, then stir in the goat's, sheep's or soya milk.

5. Heat and serve, with a topping of yogurt on each portion.

Manhattan Clam Chowder _____ E W

Serves 6

½ onion, chopped
1 stick celery, chopped
Oil, for frying
14 oz (395g) tin tomatoes
10 oz (285g) tin clams in salted water
Water
2 tablespoons (36ml) concentrated tomato purée
2 potatoes, peeled and cubed
1 bay leaf
Dash thyme
½ teaspoon (3ml) Worcester sauce
3 drops Tabasco sauce
Freshly ground black pepper

1. Gently sauté the onion and celery in a frying pan.
2. Purée the tomatoes in a food processor or handgrater, then sieve to remove the seeds.
3. Drain the clams and reserve the liquor, making it up to ½ pint (285ml) with water. Combine this liquid, the tomatoes and tomato purée in a large saucepan.
4. Add the cubed potatoes, bay leaf, thyme, Worcester and Tabasco sauces, pepper and clams. Bring to the boil and simmer until the potatoes are cooked.
5. Adjust seasonings and serve.

Jerusalem Artichoke Soup _____ E   W

Serves 8

Jerusalem artichokes are very easy to grow if you have a garden. Ask a friend who grows them to let you have some tubers, then put them where you don't mind having 6-foot high plants. Once you have Jerusalem artichokes, you will never be without them, but they are not invasive.

1¾ lb (795g) Jerusalem artichokes
¼ lb (115g) potatoes
1 onion
1 pint (570ml) stock, made from a chicken
  or vegetable stock cube
1 pint (570ml) goat's or sheep's milk or
  unsweetened soya milk
Dash nutmeg
Sea salt and freshly ground black pepper
8 tablespoons (144ml) or more of sheep's
  or goat's milk yogurt

1. Prepare the artichokes by scrubbing or
    scraping them and then slice them.
    Peel and slice the potatoes and onions.
2. Make up the stock and pour it into a
    large saucepan. Bring it to the boil,
    then add the vegetables and cook them
    until tender.
3. Sieve the vegetables and stock or purée
    them in a food processor fitted with the
    metal blade.
4. Return the soup to the saucepan and
    stir in the milk, nutmeg and seasoning.
5. Heat and serve with a dollop of yogurt
    on each portion.

Serves 5

This is one of those recipes that can be varied according to seasonal availability of vegetables and what you have in your cupboard. You may wish to substitute spaghetti broken in small pieces for one of the ingredients. Cabbage can be used instead of broccoli, and haricot, butter or kidney beans can replace black-eyed beans.

1 oz (30g) black-eyed beans, soaked overnight
½ onion, chopped
1 clove garlic, minced
1 celery stick, diced
1 leek, sliced
Oil, for frying
4 oz (115g) potato, diced
2 oz (55g) carrots, diced
2 oz (55g) broccoli, chopped small
2 oz (55g) French or runner beans, chopped
1¼ pints (710ml) water
1 teaspoon (6ml) Miso (available from health food shops)
2 dessertspoons (24ml) concentrated tomato purée
½ teaspoon (3ml) fresh basil, chopped
Sea salt and freshly ground black pepper
1½ oz (45g) hard goat's or sheep's milk cheese, finely grated

1. Boil the black-eyed beans rapidly for 10 minutes, then simmer them for 35 minutes.
2. In a small non-stick frying pan, soften the onion, garlic, celery and leek in the oil over a low heat.
3. Transfer the vegetables from the frying pan to a large saucepan. Add the potato, carrots, broccoli and French or runner beans.
4. Pour the water into the saucepan and add the Miso, tomato purée, basil and seasoning.
5. Bring the soup to the boil, then simmer for 20–30 minutes.
6. Serve with a bowl of grated cheese.

Cream of Celery Soup

Serves 4 to 5

¾ lb (340g) celery, chopped
1 medium onion, chopped
1 tablespoon (18ml) oil
1 lb (455g) potatoes, peeled and sliced
1 pint (570ml) chicken stock, made from a
cube
1 pint (570ml) goat's or sheep's milk or
unsweetened soya milk
Sea salt and pepper
Dash nutmeg
Celery tops or chopped fresh parsley

1. Prepare the celery and onion,
   reserving the celery leaves if you are
   using them as a topping for the soup.
2. In a large non-stick frying pan, sauté
   the celery and onion in the oil until
   tender.
3. Add the potatoes and chicken stock.
   Bring to the boil and simmer, covered,
   for a further 15 minutes.
4. Purée the vegetables in a handgrater,
   or in a food processor fitted with the
   metal blade, in 2 batches.
5. Pour the purée into a large saucepan,
   add the goat's, sheep's or soya milk,
   seasoning and nutmeg.
6. Heat and serve topped with chopped
   celery leaves or parsley.

Onion Soup

Serves 4

1 lb (455g) onions, sliced thinly
1 tablespoon (18ml) bacon fat
1 tablespoon (18ml) yeast extract
1¾ pints (1 litre) boiling water
Sea salt and freshly ground black pepper
2 slices bread from a loaf, or 4 slices
   French bread
1 dessertspoon (12ml) soft margarine
1 oz (30g) Feta cheese, finely grated

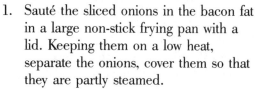

1. Sauté the sliced onions in the bacon fat in a large non-stick frying pan with a lid. Keeping them on a low heat, separate the onions, cover them so that they are partly steamed.

2. When the onions are transparent make some stock by combining the yeast extract with the boiling water. Add to the onions, bring to the boil and simmer for 15 minutes.

3. If you are using 2 slices of bread, cut them into 2 rounds each with a scone cutter. Toast these, or the 4 slices of French bread, lightly on both sides under the grill.

4. Spread the margarine on the toast and sprinkle the grated Feta cheese on top. Put the toast back under the grill and cook until the cheese bubbles.

5. Heat and serve the soup with a toasted cheese round floating on top of each bowlful.

Leek and Potato Soup _____ E W

Serves 5

This soup can also be chilled and served cold.

1 lb (455g) leeks, sliced
1 medium onion, chopped
1¼ lb (565g) potatoes, peeled and sliced
1 pint (570ml) chicken stock, made with a
   cube
15 fl oz (425ml) goat's or sheep's milk or
   unsweetened soya milk
Fresh watercress or parsley, for garnish

1. Put the leeks, onion and potatoes in a
   large saucepan. Add the stock.
2. Bring the soup to the boil and simmer
   until the vegetables are tender.
3. Sieve the soup in a handgrater.
   Alternatively liquidize it in a food
   processor fitted with the metal blade, in
   two batches.
4. Pour the purée back into the large
   saucepan. Stir in the goat's or soya
   milk.
5. Heat, season to taste and serve. Top
   each portion with watercress or
   chopped parsley.

Parsnip Soup _____ E W

Serves 5

This is good with croûtons (see the note on page 43) or a sprinkling of chopped fresh parsley.

1 lb (455g) parsnips, scrubbed and sliced
4 oz (115g) onion, chopped
1 clove garlic, minced
1 pint (570ml) stock, made from a chicken
   stock cube
1 teaspoon (6ml) mild curry powder, or to
   taste (optional)
Sea salt and freshly ground black pepper
1 pint (570ml) goat's or sheep's milk or
   unsweetened soya milk

1. Put the chopped parsnips, onion and
   garlic in a saucepan and pour in the
   stock. Bring to the boil and simmer for
   15 minutes.
2. Sieve or liquidize the vegetables and
   stock, then pour the purée back into
   the saucepan.
3. Add the curry powder, if desired, and
   the seasoning.
4. Stir the milk into the soup.
5. Bring the soup to the boil, stirring
   occasionally, and serve.

Roquefort and Vegetable Soup___E W

Serves 6

This is an unusual soup, and a good example of how a little bit of Roquefort can go a long way in a recipe.

2 onions, chopped
½ lb (225g) swede, peeled and chopped
2 sticks celery, chopped
4 oz (115g) carrots, chopped
Oil, for frying
1 pint (570ml) chicken or vegetable stock, made from a cube
1 oz (30g) Roquefort cheese
Freshly ground black pepper
Fresh parsley, chopped

1. In a large non-stick frying pan, sauté all the vegetables in the minimum of oil.
2. Add ¾ pint (425ml) of the stock to the pan and cook until the vegetables are soft.
3. Pour the soup into a handgrater, or a food processor fitted with the metal blade, then crumble the cheese on top and purée until smooth.
4. Heat in a saucepan with the rest of the stock and season with pepper. Top each serving with chopped parsley.

Chilled Cucumber and Yogurt Soup___E W

Serves 4

1 garlic clove, minced
1 tablespoon (6ml) olive oil
¼ teaspoon (1.5ml) salt
¾ pint (425ml) sheep's or goat's milk yogurt
8 fl oz (240ml) water
12 oz (340g) cucumber, peeled and cubed
Fresh mint, chopped

1. Combine the garlic clove with the olive oil and salt.
2. Beat the garlic mixture into the yogurt and then beat in the water.
3. Add the peeled and chopped cucumber and the mint
4. Chill the soup for at least an hour before serving in order to allow the flavours to develop.

Tomato and Carrot Soup E W

Serves 5–6

If you don't have any fresh parsley, stir in dried parsley when heating the soup before serving.

1 lb (455g) carrots, scrubbed and sliced
1 medium potato, peeled and sliced
1 oz (30g) margarine
1 pint (570ml) chicken or vegetable stock, made from a cube
3 tablespoons (54ml) concentrated tomato purée
Sea salt and freshly ground black pepper
1 pint (570ml) water
6 tablespoons (108ml) or more sheep's or goat's milk yogurt
1 tablespoon fresh parsley, chopped

1. Soften the carrots and potato in the margarine in a large non-stick frying pan, covered, on a medium-low heat for 5 minutes. Toss the vegetables from time to time.
2. Pour in the stock, bring the soup to the boil and simmer for 15 minutes, until the vegetables are tender.
3. Add the tomato purée and seasoning.
4. Purée the vegetables and stock in a handgrater or food processor.
5. Pour the soup into a large saucepan and stir in the water.
6. Heat and serve with a dollop of yogurt and chopped parsley for each person.

Watercress Soup E

Serves 6

2 pints (1.1 litres) chicken stock, made from a stock cube
1 lb (455g) potatoes, peeled and sliced
1 bunch of watercress (4 oz/115g), roughly chopped
2 oz (55g) margarine
1 tablespoon (18ml) flour
¾ pint (425ml) goat's or sheep's milk or unsweetened soya milk
Sea salt and freshly ground black pepper
Dash nutmeg

1. Make the chicken stock and pour it into a large saucepan. Put the potatoes in the pan and cook them in the stock for five minutes.
2. Add the watercress, reserving a few leaves for garnish. Simmer until the potatoes are cooked.
3. Purée the soup in a food processor or handgrater.
4. Make a white sauce by melting the margarine over a low heat, stirring in

the flour and then the milk, cooking until thickened.

5. Gradually add the vegetable purée to the stock. Season with salt, pepper and nutmeg, to taste.

6. Serve topped with a few watercress leaves.

Chilled Avocado and Yogurt Soup_____E W

Serves 4

This is very quick to make on a hot summer's day when you don't feel like cooking.

1 avocado (about 8 oz/225g)
1 teaspoon (6ml) lime juice
8 oz (225g) tub sheep's or goat's milk
   yogurt
1 small vegetable stock cube
½ pint (285ml) water
Fresh parsley, chopped

1. Peel the avocado, chop it roughly and dribble the lime juice over it.

2. Purée the avocado with the yogurt, either by mashing or by mixing in a food processor fitted with the metal blade.

3. Dissolve the stock cube in a small amount of hot water, and make up the rest with cold water. When the stock has completely cooled, stir the stock into the avocado yogurt mixture and chill.

4. To serve, garnish each portion with a sprinkling of fresh parsley.

FISH MAIN COURSES

Since having to cater for a dairy-product-free diet, I've found that we are eating a greater variety of fish than we used to. It's amazing how quick some of these recipes are to prepare, especially Seafood Risotto, Prawn Creole, Fish Bake, Spaghetti with Clam Sauce and the fish salads. Where tinned fish or shellfish are listed in the ingredients, it is usually for the sake of convenience. If you want to use fresh fish, just substitute the same weight given for tinned. The hot fish dishes are at the beginning of this chapter and quiches and salads are at the end. Recipes for fish pâtés and spreads can be found in chapter 3, Appetizers.

Seafood Risotto _____ E W

Serves 3

½ onion, chopped
1 clove garlic, minced
1 tablespoon (18ml) olive oil
3 tablespoons (54ml) green pepper, diced
2 oz (55g) mushrooms, sliced
1 pint (570ml) chicken stock, made from a cube
½ lb (225g) Italian rice
2 oz (55g) shrimps or prawns, cooked
7 oz (200g) tin cockles, drained and rinsed
1 tablespoon (18ml) fresh parsley, chopped
Freshly ground black pepper

1. In a large non-stick frying pan, sauté the onion and garlic in the olive oil.
2. Add the green pepper and mushrooms, and cook gently, tossing frequently.
3. Pour in the chicken stock and rice, and bring the risotto to the boil.
4. Stir in the prawns and cockles and simmer, stirring occasionally until all the liquid is absorbed and the rice is cooked.
5. Just before serving, stir in the chopped fresh parsley.

Shrimp Curry

Serves 4

10 oz (285g) shrimps or prawns, cleaned and cooked

1 onion, chopped

1 clove garlic, minced

2 sticks celery, sliced

Oil, for frying

1½ oz (45g) margarine

1½ oz (45g) plain flour

1 tablespoon (18ml) mild Madras curry powder

1 pint (570ml) goat's or sheep's milk or unsweetened soya milk

3 tablespoons (54ml) sherry

Sea salt and freshly ground black pepper

1. In a small non-stick frying pan, sauté the onion, garlic and celery over a low heat until they are tender.
2. In a saucepan make a white sauce by melting the margarine, stirring in the flour mixed with the curry powder, and then the milk. Stir until thickened over a medium low heat.
3. Add the sherry to the curried white sauce, then the onion, garlic, celery and the cooked shrimps or prawns. Season to taste.
4. Heat and serve on a bed of rice.

Salmon Fish Cakes

Serves 4

½ lb (225g) potatoes, peeled and sliced

2 oz (55g) Feta cheese

1×7 oz (200g) tin salmon

1 egg

Sea salt and freshly ground black pepper

1 tablespoon (18ml) fresh parsley, chopped

Breadcrumbs or flour, for coating

Oil, for frying

1. Cook the potatoes, drain, and mash them in a bowl.
2. Stir the finely grated cheese into the potatoes.
3. Flake the salmon into the bowl.
4. Beat the egg and add it to the mixture. Season to taste. Add the parsley.
5. With floured hands, shape the mixture into 4 cakes and coat them on both sides with breadcrumbs or flour.
6. Fry the fish cakes in the minimum of oil in a large non-stick frying pan. Cook for a few minutes over a medium heat until they are browned and well heated.

Kulebyakas

Serves 6

These are rather fiddly for a family meal, but they make a cheap yet impressive dinner party dish. They can also be served cold.

1 lb (455g) spinach, fresh or frozen
1½ oz (45g) margarine
1 egg, beaten
1 onion, chopped
¼ lb (115g) button mushrooms
Oil, for frying
1×14 oz (395g) tin tomatoes
1×1 lb (455g) pack frozen puff pastry, thawed
1×7½ oz (215g) and 1×3 oz (85g) tins salmon
Sea salt and freshly ground black pepper
3 tablespoons (54ml) lemon juice
Watercress, for garnish

1. Preheat the oven to 425°F/220°C (Gas Mark 7). Chop the spinach if using fresh.
2. Cook the fresh or frozen spinach and squeeze out the excess liquid.
3. Melt ½ oz (15g) of the margarine and stir it into the spinach. When the spinach has cooled, add half the beaten egg to it.
4. In a small non-stick frying pan, sauté the onion and mushrooms in a little oil.
5. Strain off the juice from the tinned tomatoes and discard it. Chop the tomatoes roughly.
6. Roll out two slabs of puff pastry to rectangles measuring 11×8 inches (28×20.5cm).
7. Keeping well away from the edges, layer up the onions, mushrooms, tomatoes, spinach and salmon lengthwise down the centre of each pastry rectangle. Season.
8. Brush one of the long edges with some more of the beaten egg, then roll the dry edge of the pastry over the wet edge, and press them together, as if making a sausage roll. Tuck in the top and bottom, and place the kulebyaka

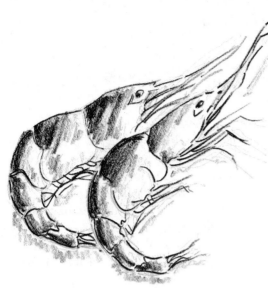

on a greased baking tray. Repeat with the other kulebyaka.

9. Brush the pastry with the remainder of the beaten egg, and slash across the tops 3 or 4 times.

10. Bake for 30–40 minutes, or until golden brown.

11. Remove the kulebyakas from the oven, and melt the remaining 1 oz (30g) margarine and combine it with the lemon juice. Pour this mixture into the slashes in the pastry.

12. Serve both kulebyakas side by side on a platter, garnished with watercress.

Prawn Creole _____ E W

Serves 3

The same amount of cooked shrimps or a 6½–7½ oz (185–215g) tin of tuna can be used in place of the prawns.

1 onion, chopped
1 clove garlic, minced
Oil, for frying
1 stick celery, sliced
4 oz (115g) green pepper, cut in small strips
1×14 oz (395g) tin tomatoes
2 tablespoons (36ml) concentrated tomato purée
½ teaspoon (3ml) Worcester sauce
6 oz (170g) cooked prawns
Sea salt and freshly ground black pepper

1. Sauté the onion and garlic in a large non-stick frying pan, then add the celery and green pepper. Cook until tender.

2. Chop the tomatoes roughly while still inside the tin, then pour them into the frying pan.

3. Add the tomato purée, Worcester sauce and cooked prawns. Season.

4. Serve on a bed of rice or noodles.

Haddock Crumble   E

Serves 3-4

For the haddock and parsley sauce:

¾-1lb (340-455g) fresh haddock
1 pint (570ml) goat's or sheep's milk or
  unsweetened soya milk
Sea salt and freshly ground black pepper
½ oz (15g) margarine
2 oz (55g) onion, chopped
1½ oz (45g) margarine
1½ oz (45g) flour
1 teaspoon (6ml) English mustard powder
1½ oz (45g) fresh parsley, chopped

For the crumble topping:

2 oz (55g) porridge oats
1 oz (30g) margarine
2 oz (55g) Feta cheese, finely grated

1. Preheat the oven to 425°F/220°C
   (Gas Mark 7), and lightly grease an
   oval 2-pint (1.1 litre) pie dish.
2. Poach the haddock in the milk in a
   large non-stick frying pan over a
   medium heat. Add the seasoning and
   cook until the fish flakes.
3. Put the cooked fish in the pie dish,
   reserving the milk and fish stock for
   the parsley sauce.
4. Melt the ½ oz (15g) margarine in a
   saucepan and sauté the chopped onion
   in it. Place the cooked onions on top of
   the fish.
5. Using the same saucepan, melt the 1½
   oz (45g) margarine and stir in the flour
   and mustard. Gradually incorporate the
   milk, whisking the sauce over a
   medium-low heat. When the sauce has
   boiled and thickened, stir in the
   parsley.
6. Pour the parsley sauce over the fish,
   then rub the crumble ingredients
   together, and distribute over the top.
7. Bake for 15-20 minutes, or until the
   sauce is bubbling and the crumble is
   golden.

Fish Bake

Serves 4

This is a plain but tasty dish, quick and easy to prepare.

1 lb (455g) fillets of haddock or other
white fish
1 onion, chopped
1 clove garlic, chopped (optional)
Oil, for frying
2×14 oz (395g) tins tomatoes
1 bay leaf
Pinch dried dill
Sea salt and freshly ground black pepper
3 oz (85g) dried breadcrumbs
3 oz (85g) Feta cheese, coarsely grated

1. Preheat the oven to 375°F/190°C (Gas Mark 5).
2. Grease an 8×12-inch (25.5×30.5cm) shallow casserole and place the fish in it, skin side down.
3. Sauté the onion and garlic (if desired) in a little oil in a small non-stick frying pan. Distribute them on top of the fish.
4. Roughly chop the tomatoes and add them to the casserole. Place the bay leaf in the centre and sprinkle the dill over the top.
5. Top with the breadcrumbs and grated cheese.
6. Bake for 30 minutes, or until the fish is firm and flakes easily.

Fried Haddock or Plaice

Serves 4

2½ oz (70g) homemade dried
breadcrumbs
1 lb (455g) haddock or plaice
1 egg, beaten
Oil, for frying

1. Preheat the oven to 275°F/140°C (Gas Mark 1).
2. Make the breadcrumbs by putting the bread in a food processor fitted with the metal blade. Whizz until the crumbs are very fine. Put them in a shallow baking tin to dry slowly in the oven, for about 15 minutes.
3. Wash the fish fillets and dry them, then dip them in the beaten egg.
4. Roll both sides of the fish in breadcrumbs
5. Fry until the fish flakes.

Kedgeree

Serves 4

Try to find a fishmonger who supplies naturally smoked and not dyed haddock. Kedgeree is useful as a supper, lunch or brunch dish, but I have yet to get up early enough to make it for breakfast.

2 eggs
1 lb (455g) smoked haddock
1 pint (570ml) goat's or sheep's milk or
    unsweetened soya milk
1½ oz (45g) margarine
1½ oz (45g) flour
1 teaspoon (6ml) mild Madras curry
    powder, or to taste
Freshly ground black pepper

1. Hard boil the eggs and leave them to cool.
2. Poach the smoked haddock in the goat's or soya milk, bringing it to the boil and them simmering it for 10 minutes. Remove the fish and reserve the fish and milk stock.
3. Skin and flake the fish, removing the bones.
4. Melt the margarine, stir in the flour and curry powder, and gradually whisk in the fish and milk stock. Stir the sauce over a medium low heat until it boils and thickens.
5. Slice the hard-boiled eggs in half and remove the yolks. Chop the whites of the eggs and add them to the sauce.
6. Stir the flaked fish and pepper into the sauce.
7. Grate the yolks of the eggs finely in a hand grater. Reserve.
8. Heat the kedgeree and serve on a bed of rice, with the grated egg yolk on top.

Spaghetti with Clam Sauce

Serves 4

This is practically an instant meal that you can make from store cupboard ingredients.

Sea salt
2 tablespoons (36ml) olive oil
4 cloves garlic, minced
2×10 oz (285g) tins baby clams in salted water
1 lb (455g) spaghetti
4 tablespoons (72ml) fresh parsley, chopped
8 tablespoons (144ml) concentrated tomato purée
8 fl oz (240ml) reserved liquor from the clams
Freshly ground black pepper
1–2 oz (30–55g) finely grated hard sheep's or goat's milk cheese, as required (optional)

1. Heat a large pan of salted water for the spaghetti.
2. Put the olive oil and minced garlic in a frying pan. Drain the clams, reserving the liquid, then put the clams in the pan. Sauté for 5–10 minutes.
3. Start cooking the spaghetti. Add it to the boiling water, stir, and bring it back to the boil. Reduce the heat and simmer for 9 minutes.
4. In the meantime, add the chopped parsley, tomato purée and clam liquor to the frying pan. Season with pepper. Cook the clam sauce over a medium heat, stirring frequently, while the spaghetti cooks.
5. Drain the spaghetti and put it on a platter or on individual plates. Pour the clam sauce on top. Serve with or without grated cheese, passed separately.

Grilled Sardines _____ E

Serves 4

The taste of these fish is strong, but the lemon juice, brown bread and margarine help to tone it down. The kitchen smells of the seaside while they are cooking.

1¼ lb (565g) fresh sardines
Seasoned flour, to coat
A little vegetable oil
Lemon wedges
Brown bread and margarine

1. Pre-heat the grill.
2. Prepare the fish by chopping off the heads and tails, slitting them down the belly and cleaning them. Rinse them under the cold tap.
3. Spread the fish open and flatten them, then dredge them in seasoned flour.
4. Brush the grill rack with oil and place the fish on the rack.
5. Grill for up to 10 minutes, turning once.
6. Serve immediately with lemon wedges, brown bread and margarine.

Scotch Woodcock _____

Serves 4

This lunch or supper dish was inspired by one of Mrs Beeton's recipes, in which anchovy paste is used instead of pilchard and tomato spread. The resulting adaptation is still rich in calcium and vitamin D, but it is not as salty as the original.

Pilchard and Tomato Spread (see the recipe on page 36)
6 eggs
3 fl oz (90ml) goat's or sheep's milk or unsweetened soya milk
Freshly ground black pepper
4 slices toast

1. Make the Pilchard and Tomato Spread in the same quantities as the recipe.
2. Beat the eggs and milk together and season with pepper.
3. Make the toast and scramble the eggs.
4. Spread the pilchard and tomato spread on the toast and put the scrambled egg on top.

5. Serve immediately, with more toast on the side.

Salmon, Cheese and Mushroom Quiche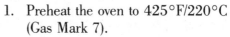

Serves 6

1×8-inch (20.5cm) pastry case, uncooked
1 small onion, chopped
5 oz (140g) mushrooms, sliced
Oil, for frying
3 eggs
7 fl oz (200ml) goat's milk or sheep's milk
  or unsweetened soya milk
Freshly ground black pepper
1×7 oz (200g) tin salmon
3 oz (85g) Feta cheese, finely grated

1. Preheat the oven to 425°F/220°C (Gas Mark 7).
2. Bake the pastry case blind for 10 minutes (see the note on page 99).
3. In a small non-stick frying pan, sauté the onion, then add the sliced mushrooms. Simmer, tossing occasionally, until cooked.
4. In a bowl, whisk the eggs, then add the goat's, sheep's or soya milk and whisk some more. Season with pepper.
6. Open the can of salmon and discard the skin. Mix the salmon with the onions and mushrooms, and distribute this mixture on the bottom of the pastry case.
7. Spread the grated cheese over the salmon, then pour in the egg custard.
8. Bake at the pre-heated setting for 10 minutes, then turn the oven down to 350°F/180°C (Gas Mark 4) for 20 minutes, or until the quiche is golden and set.
9. Serve hot or cold.

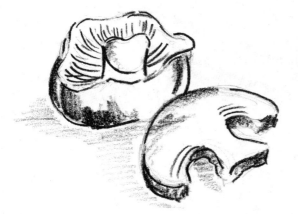

Tuna and Cucumber Quiche _____ E

Serves 4

1×8-inch (20.5cm) pastry case, uncooked
1×6½-7½ oz (185–215g) tin tuna
2-inch (5cm) piece cucumber, skinned and
   cubed
4 tablespoons (72ml) mayonnaise
7 tablespoons (126ml) sheep's or goat's
   milk yogurt
2 teaspoons (12ml) gelatine
2 tablespoons (36ml) warm water
12 cucumber slices

1. Bake the pastry case blind for a total of 20 minutes and let it cool (see the note on page 99).
2. Drain the tuna and flake it into a bowl. Mix in the cubed cucumber, mayonnaise and yogurt.
3. Sprinkle the gelatine on to the warm water in a mug. Place the mug in a saucepan of water and heat gently until the gelatine dissolves. Let it cool but don't allow it to set.
4. Stir the gelatine into the tuna mixture.
5. Pour the filling into the pastry case. Arrange the cucumber slices on top.
6. Chill or leave in a cool place until the filling is set.
7. Serve cold with salads.

Crab Mousse _____ W

Serves 4

I have made the servings of this recipe small because although it is tasty, crab is very filling. You may wish to double the recipe and put it in a 1 pint (570ml) soufflé dish.

6 oz (170g) tin crabmeat
2 tablespoons (36ml) mayonnaise
5 tablespoons (90ml) sheep's or goat's milk
   yogurt
1 tablespoon (18ml) lemon juice
1 tablespoon (18ml) fresh parsley, chopped
1 tablespoon (18ml) fresh chives, chopped
½ teaspoon (3ml) French mustard
1 teaspoon (6ml) gelatine
1 tablespoon (18ml) warm water

1. Rinse and drain the crabmeat well, and put it in a small bowl.

2. Using a fork, stir the mayonnaise, yogurt, lemon juice, herbs and French mustard into the crabmeat.

3. Sprinkle the gelatine on to the warm water in a mug. Stand the mug in a saucepan of water on a low heat and stir until the gelatine dissolves.

4. Stir the gelatine into the other ingredients, and pour the mousse into a ½-pint (285ml) serving bowl. Chill until set.

Tuna and Kidney Bean Salad_____E W

Serves 4

Chives can be substituted for the spring onions.

7 oz (200g) dried kidney beans, soaked
  overnight, *or* 1×14 oz (395g) tin kidney
  beans, drained
1×6½-7½ oz (185-215g) tin tuna,
  drained and flaked
3 sticks celery, split lengthwise and sliced
2 spring onions, sliced
2 oz (55g) green pepper, chopped
2 tablespoons (36ml) fresh parsley,
  chopped
Freshly ground black pepper
French Dressing, to taste (see page 122)

1. If using dried kidney beans, soak them
   in water overnight or for 8 hours. Boil
   them rapidly for 10 minutes, then
   simmer for a further 40 minutes. Drain
   and leave them to cool.
2. Combine all the ingredients in a bowl
   and leave the salad for an hour or two
   to enable the flavours to develop.
3. Serve as a main course salad, or
   leaving out the tuna, as a side salad for
   five people.

Special Tuna Salad _____E W

Serves 3

1×6½-7½ oz (185–215g) tin tuna,
  drained and flaked
2 tablespoons (35ml) sheep's or goat's
  milk yogurt
½ oz (15g) gherkin or picked cucumber,
  minced
1 spring onion, minced
Freshly ground black pepper
A few lettuce leaves
Fresh parsley, chopped

1. Combine the first 5 ingredients
2. Serve on a bed of lettuce with a
   sprinkling of parsley on top, or use as a
   sandwich filling.

Salade Niçoise _____ E W

Serves 4

The colourful layers of this delicious salad are shown to their best advantage in a glass bowl.

8 anchovies
A little goat's or sheep's milk or unsweetened soya milk
½ lb (225g) firm potatoes (new potatoes or Desirée)
Sea salt
6 oz (170g) French beans
2 oz (55g) green pepper
2 tomatoes
6½–7½ oz (185–215g) tin tuna
8 black or green olives
Freshly ground black pepper
French Dressing, to taste (see page 122)
Fresh parsley, chopped or chives (optional)

1. Soak the anchovies in goat's milk or sugarless soya milk, in order to make them less salty.
2. Scrub the potatoes, slice them thinly, and cook them with a little salt until just tender.
3. Top and tail the French beans. If they are small and thin, leave them whole, otherwise, slice them into 1-inch (2.5cm) pieces. Cook the beans with a little salt until barely tender.
4. Slice the green pepper in rings and cut the tomatoes into wedges.
5. In a broad-bottomed 2-pint (1.1 litre) bowl, layer the potatoes, beans, tuna, green pepper, tomatoes, olives and drained anchovies, dribbling on French dressing as you go and seasoning with pepper.
5. Garnish with parsley or chives, if desired, and serve.

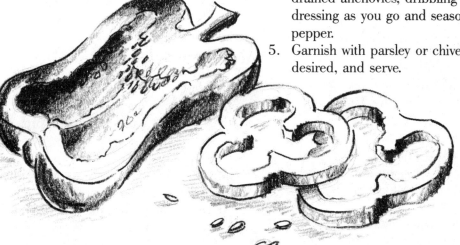

MEAT AND POULTRY MAIN COURSES

Cooking without using cow's milk does not mean that many of your favourite foods must be sacrificed. You may be surprised to find that the following recipes for some popular dishes, e.g., Moussaka, Lasagne and Boeuf Stroganoff can be just as delicious when made without cow's milk products. This chapter consists mostly of casseroles, in which the meat or poultry is combined with Feta cheese, yogurt, goat's, ewe's or soya milk, breadcrumbs, cabbage, broccoli, chick peas and parsley or root vegetables. The recipes range from several that are elegant enough for a dinner party to some made with left-over meat.

Moussaka _____ E

Serves 6

This takes about an hour to assemble, which to my mind is too long for a family meal, but it is a good dish to serve to guests.

For the filling:

1½ lb (680g) aubergines
Sea salt
Olive oil, for frying
1 clove garlic, minced
2 onions, chopped
1½ lb (680g) lean minced lamb
3 tablespoons (54ml) concentrated
  tomato purée
1 dessertspoon (12ml) fresh mint,
  chopped *or* 1 teaspoon (6ml) dried
3 tablespoons (54ml) fresh parsley,
  chopped
¼ pint (140ml) stock made with
  1 teaspoon (6ml) yeast extract

1. Slice the aubergines thinly, layer them in a colander, and sprinkle each layer with salt. leave them for 20 minutes while the bitter juices run out.
2. Preheat the oven to 375°F/190°C (Gas Mark 5).
3. In a large non-stick frying pan, sauté the garlic and onion in the olive oil, then add the minced lamb and brown it. Drain off any excess fat.
4. Add the tomato purée, mint, parsley and stock. Bring the mixture to the boil and simmer for five minutes.
5. Rinse and drain the aubergine slices, then sauté them in the minimum of olive oil in a large non-stick frying pan.

For the topping:

2 oz (55g) margarine
2 oz (55g) flour
Dash nutmeg
Dash cinnamon
Sea salt and freshly ground black
   pepper
¾ pint (425ml) goat's or sheep's
   milk or unsweetened soya milk
3 oz (85g) Feta cheese, finely grated

6. Melt the margarine for the topping in a
   saucepan. Let it cool slightly, then stir
   in the flour, cinnamon, nutmeg and
   seasoning. Add the goat's, sheep's or
   soya milk gradually, while stirring over
   a medium-low heat. Let the sauce boil
   and thicken.
7. Put a layer of aubergines at the bottom
   of a 9×12×2-inch (23×31×5cm)
   casserole.
8. Cover the aubergines with some of the
   meat mixture, and repeat, finishing
   with a layer of aubergines.
9. Pour the white sauce evenly over the
   top and sprinkle on the Feta cheese.
   Freeze at this point if desired.
10. Bake for about 45 minutes, or until
    golden and bubbling, then serve.

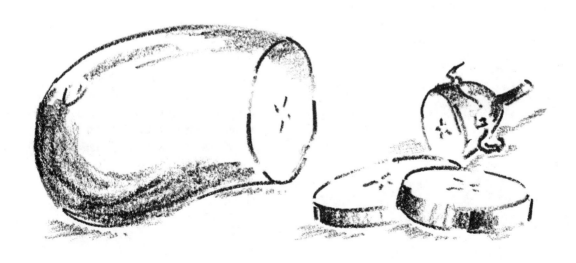

Potato Moussaka

Serves 4–5

This is much quicker to make than the usual moussaka.

1½ lb (680g) firm potatoes
Sea salt
1 onion, chopped
1 small garlic clove, minced
1 stick celery, minced
Olive oil, for frying
¾ lb (340g) lean minced lamb
1×14oz (395g) tin tomatoes
2 tablespoons (36ml) concentrated tomato
  purée
2 dessertspoons (24ml) fresh parsley,
  chopped
Sea salt and freshly ground black pepper
3 tablespoons (54ml) dried homemade
  breadcrumbs
3 oz (85g) Feta cheese, coarsely grated

1. Preheat the oven to 375°F/190°C (Gas Mark 5).
2. Slice the potatoes thinly, season them with salt, and cook them until they are just tender.
3. In a large non-stick frying pan, sauté the onion, garlic and celery in a little olive oil.
4. Add the lamb and brown it. Drain off any excess fat.
5. Chop the tomatoes roughly while they are still inside the tin, then add them with their juice to the contents of the frying pan. Stir in the tomato purée, parsley and seasoning.
6. Bring the sauce to the boil and simmer it for 5 minutes.
7. Lightly oil a 3-pint (1.7 litre) casserole and coat the bottom of it with breadcrumbs.
8. Layer the potatoes and sauce alternately, starting and finishing with potatoes. Sprinkle the Feta cheese on top. *Freeze at this point if desired.*
9. Cook, covered, for about 40 minutes.

Lamb Burgers

Serves 4

These are delicious barbecued.

1 lb (455g) lean minced lamb
Sea salt
2 dessertspoons (24ml) fresh mint, chopped
8 tablespoons (144ml) sheep's or goat's milk yogurt
4 sesame seed buns
4 lettuce leaves
1 pickled cucumber, sliced crosswise
2 tomatoes, sliced

1. Preheat the grill.
2. Season the lamb with salt and shape it into 4 burgers.
3. Put the lamb burgers on the wire rack of the grill pan, and cook them for 25–30 minutes, turning once.
4. Meanwhile chop the mint fine and mix it with the yogurt. Put the sauce in a small bowl.
5. Slice the sesame seed buns in half and warm them under the grill for the last few minutes of the lamb burgers' cooking time.
6. When the burgers are cooked, place a lettuce leaf on the bottom half of each bun, then put the lamb burger on top. Arrange tomato and pickle slices on top of the burgers, then put the top half of the bun on top of that.
7. Serve the burgers and pass the yogurt and mint sauce in place of ketchup.

Lamb Curry

Serves 5-6

1 onion, chopped
2 sticks celery, sliced
Oil, for frying
2 oz (55g) margarine
2 oz (55g) plain flour
2 tablespoons (54ml) mild Madras curry powder, or more, to taste
Dash ginger
Dash ground cloves
Dash thyme
1¼ pints (710ml) goat's or sheep's milk or unsweetened soya milk
¾ lb (340g) left-over roast lamb, cut into chunks
2 tablespoons (36ml) fresh parsley, chopped
Sea salt and fresh ground black pepper
Sultanas or raisins

1. Sauté the onion and celery in the minimum of oil in a small non-stick frying pan.
2. Meanwhile melt the margarine in a saucepan. Let it cool slightly, then stir in the flour, spices and thyme, and then the goat's, sheep's or soya milk. Stirring constantly, bring the sauce to the boil over a medium low heat.
3. Add the onion, celery, lamb chunks, parsley and seasoning to the sauce. *Freeze at this point if desired.*
4. Heat the curry thoroughly and serve it on a bed of rice. Pass a bowl of sultanas or raisins to go with it.

Stuffed Cabbage _____ E W

Serves 3-4

6-8 cabbage leaves (Savoy is best)
½ lb (225g) raw minced lamb or beef
5 tablespoons (90ml) uncooked rice
1 clove garlic, minced
½ teaspoon (3ml) dried thyme
1 teaspoon (6ml) lemon juice
Sea salt and freshly ground black pepper
1 pint (570ml) tomato juice

1. Preheat the oven to 350°F/180°C (Gas Mark 4).
2. Wash the cabbage leaves, then steam them until they wilt. Remove them from the heat.
3. Meanwhile mix the meat, rice, garlic, thyme, lemon juice and seasoning in a bowl.
4. When the cabbage is cool enough to handle, cut out the thick ribs and discard, and slice any very big leaves in half.
5. Put a small amount of meat mixture at one end of each leaf, keeping the filling away from the sides. Tuck in the sides while rolling up each parcel.
6. Prepare a 2 pint (1.1 litre) casserole with a lid by coating the bottom of it with a little tomato juice.
7. Pack the stuffed cabbage leaves tightly into the casserole, then pour the rest of the tomato juice on top.
8. Bake, covered, for 1 hour. Serve.

Boeuf Stroganoff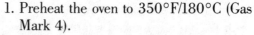

Serves 6

1 onion, chopped
Oil, for frying
½ lb (225g) mushrooms, sliced
2 lb (900g) stewing steak, cubed
9 tablespoons (162ml) sherry
2 oz (55g) flour
1½ tablespoons (27ml) lemon juice
4 tablespoons (72ml) concentrated tomato
 purée
1 teaspoon (6ml) Worcester sauce
1 teaspoon (6ml) dry mustard
1 pint (570ml) stock, made with
 1 teaspoon (6ml) yeast extract
Sea salt and pepper
6 tablespoons (108ml) sheep's or goat's
 milk yogurt

1. Preheat the oven to 350°F/180°C (Gas Mark 4).
2. Sauté the onion in a little oil in a large non-stick frying pan with a lid.
3. Add the mushrooms and brown them. Remove the vegetables to a 3-pint (1.7 litre) casserole.
4. Brown the meat in the pan juices on a high heat.
5. Add the sherry to the meat, bring it to the boil, and simmer for 5 minutes.
6. Let the meat cool slightly, then stir in the flour.
7. Mix together the lemon juice, tomato purée, Worcester sauce and mustard. Pour this mixture into the frying pan, then stir in the stock. Season with sea salt and freshly ground black pepper.
8. Mix the meat and sauce with the onions and mushrooms in the casserole, and put the dish in the oven.
9. Cook the Boeuf Stroganoff for 1½-2 hours, or until the meat is tender. *Freeze at this point if desired.*
10. Remove the casserole from the oven and stir in the yogurt when the sauce is no longer bubbling. More yogurt can be added to taste.
11. Serve on noodles or rice.

Liver Stroganoff E

Serves 4–5

1 onion, chopped
Oil, for frying
4 oz (115g) mushrooms, sliced
1 lb (455g) lamb's liver, cut in thin strips
4 tablespoons (72ml) sherry
1½ oz (45g) flour
1 tablespoon (18ml) lemon juice
3 tablespoons (54ml) concentrated tomato
   purée
1 teaspoon (6ml) Worcester sauce
1 teaspoon (6ml) dry mustard
1 pint (570ml) stock, made with
   1 teaspoon (6ml) yeast extract
Sea salt and pepper
5 tablespoons (90ml) sheep's or goat's
   milk yogurt

1. Preheat the oven to 350°F/180°C (Gas Mark 4).
2. Sauté the onion in a little oil in a large non-stick frying pan with a lid.
3. Add the mushrooms and brown them. Remove the vegetables to a 3-pint (1.7 litre) casserole.
4. Brown the meat in the pan juices on a high heat.
5. Add the sherry to the meat, bring it to the boil, and simmer for 5 minutes.
6. Let the meat cool slightly, then stir in the flour.
7. Mix together the lemon juice, tomato purée, Worcester sauce and mustard. Pour this mixture into the frying pan, then stir in the stock. Season with sea salt and freshly ground black pepper.
8. Mix the meat and sauce with the onions and mushrooms in the casserole, and put the dish in the oven.
9. Cook the Liver Stroganoff for 1–1¼ hours. *Freeze at this point if desired.*
10. Remove the casserole from the oven and stir in the yogurt when the sauce is no longer bubbling. More yogurt can be added to taste.
11. Serve on noodles or rice.

Lasagne

Serves 6

Lasagne can also be made as a vegetarian dish, by substituting textured vegetable protein (TVP) or fresh cooked mixed vegetables for the minced beef, or by adding minced tofu to the white sauce.

For the Bolognese Sauce:

1 clove garlic, minced
1 onion, chopped
Oil, for frying
¼ lb (115g) mushrooms, sliced
1 lb (455g) lean minced beef
2×14 oz (395g) tins tomatoes
6 tablespoons (108ml) concentrated tomato purée
1 teaspoon (6ml) thyme
2 teaspoons (12ml) oregano
Sea salt and freshly ground black pepper

For the white sauce:

2 oz (55g) margarine
2 oz (55g) flour
1 teaspoon (6ml) nutmeg
1½ pints (850ml) goat's or sheep's milk or unsweetened soya milk
Sea salt and freshly ground black pepper
½×13 oz (375g) box of no-cook lasagne
4 oz (115g) coarsely grated Feta cheese

1. Preheat the oven to 375°F/190°C (Gas Mark 5).
2. In a large non-stick frying pan with a lid, sauté the garlic and onion in a little oil. Add the mushrooms and cook them until they wilt.
3. Brown the minced beef in the frying pan. Drain off any excess fat.
4. Chop the tomatoes roughly, then add them to the pan. Stir in the tomato purée, thyme and oregano. Season to taste.
5. Bring the sauce to the boil and simmer it, covered, while you make the white sauce.
6. In a medium saucepan, melt the margarine. Let it cool slightly, then stir in the flour and nutmeg. Using a whisk, incorporate the goat's, sheep's or soya milk. Season.
7. Cook the white sauce over a medium-low heat, stirring all the time, until it boils and thickens.
8. Moisten the bottom of a 9×12×2-inch (23×31×5cm) oblong casserole with some of the Bolognese Sauce.
9. Cover the bottom of the casserole with sheets of lasagne, then pour ½ the Bolognese Sauce over.

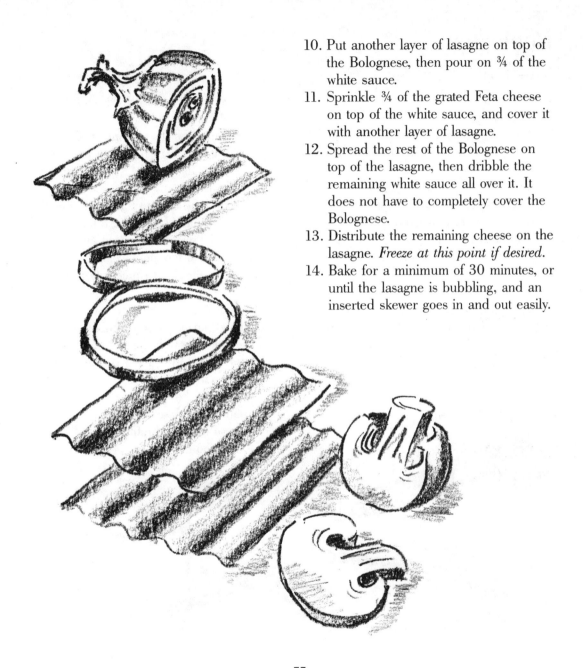

10. Put another layer of lasagne on top of the Bolognese, then pour on ¾ of the white sauce.
11. Sprinkle ¾ of the grated Feta cheese on top of the white sauce, and cover it with another layer of lasagne.
12. Spread the rest of the Bolognese on top of the lasagne, then dribble the remaining white sauce all over it. It does not have to completely cover the Bolognese.
13. Distribute the remaining cheese on the lasagne. *Freeze at this point if desired.*
14. Bake for a minimum of 30 minutes, or until the lasagne is bubbling, and an inserted skewer goes in and out easily.

Beef Stew

Serves 4-5

1 lb (455g) lean stewing steak
Oil, for frying
2 tablespoons (36ml) flour
3 tablespoons (54ml) concentrated tomato
   purée
1¼ pint (710ml) stock made from
   1 teaspoon (6ml) yeast extract
1 medium onion, quartered
1 stick celery, sliced
½ lb (225g) carrots, sliced lengthwise
6 oz (170g) swede, cubed
1 bouquet garni
Sprig of fresh parsley, tied in a bundle
Sea salt and freshly ground black pepper

1. Preheat the oven to 350°F/180°C (Gas Mark 4).
2. Trim and cube the stewing steak, and brown it on a high heat in a little oil, using a small non-stick frying pan. Let it cool slightly.
3. Sprinkle the flour on the meat and stir it in. Gradually stir in the tomato purée and stock. Bring to the boil and simmer for a few minutes.
4. Pour the meat and sauce into a 3-pint (1.7 litre) casserole.
5. Add the onion, celery, carrots, swede, bouquet garni, parsley and seasoning.
6. Cover and cook in the oven for 2-2¼ hours, or until the meat is tender and the vegetables are cooked.
7. Remove the bouquet garni and bundle of parsley, then serve in large soup bowls so that the broth can be eaten with a spoon.

Chick Pea Mince and Carrots _____ E

Serves 4

The blend of flavours in this dish masks the strong taste that chick peas usually have. My family likes this, even though they say they don't like chick peas. If you're in a hurry you can substitute 8 oz (225g) pre-cooked tinned chick peas for the dried ones.

4 oz (115g) chick peas, soaked overnight
1 onion, chopped
Oil, for frying
½ lb (225g) lean minced beef
½ lb (225g) carrots, scrubbed and sliced
1 teaspoon (6ml) yeast extract
Carrot stock, made up with water to
　15 fl oz (425ml)
2 tablespoons (36ml) flour
2 tablespoons (36ml) concentrated tomato
　purée
½ teaspoon (3ml) Worcester sauce
Sea salt and freshly ground black pepper

1. Drain the soaked chick peas and rinse them. Cook them in water for 1½ hours, or for 30–40 minutes if they are split chick peas.
2. Sauté the onion in oil in a large non-stick frying pan. Add the minced beef and brown it. Drain off any excess fat and leave it to cool slightly.
3. Meanwhile steam the carrots until they are just beginning to be tender. Reserve the carrot stock.
4. Mix the carrot stock with the yeast extract, and make the liquid up to 15 fl oz (425ml) with water.
5. Sprinkle the flour on the meat and onion in the frying pan and stir in the stock. Cook on a low heat until blended.
6. Add the tomato purée, Worcester sauce, seasoning, cooked chick peas and carrots. Stir.
7. Heat until the sauce is thickened, then simmer on a low heat for 5–10 minutes.
8. Serve with noodles, mashed potatoes or rice.

Pork and Bean Casserole

Serves 4

3 oz (85g) dried butter beans, soaked
  overnight
2 oz (55g) dried kidney beans, soaked
  overnight
Olive oil, for frying
½ lb (225g) onions, chopped
1 lb (455g) hand of pork, trimmed and
  cubed
1 oz (30g) flour
Sea salt and freshly ground black pepper
1 tablespoon (18ml) tomato purée
¾ pint (425ml) stock made from
  1 teaspoon (6ml) yeast extract
2 tablespoons (36ml) fresh parsley,
  chopped

1. Drain the beans and put them in a
   saucepan with enough water to cover
   them.
2. Boil the beans rapidly for 10 minutes,
   then turn the heat down and simmer
   them for another 10 minutes.
3. Preheat the oven to 350°F/180°C
   Gas Mark 4).
4. Sauté the chopped onions in a little
   olive oil in a large non-stick frying pan.
   Remove them to a 3-pint (1.7 litre)
   casserole.
5. Brown the meat quickly on a high heat
   in the juices in the frying pan. Let it
   cool for a minute or two once it has
   browned.
6. Sprinkle the flour on the meat and
   season.
7. Stir the tomato purée and stock into
   the meat.
8. Put the meat, sauce and beans into the
   casserole, and stir in the parsley.
9. Cook for a minimum of 1½ hours, or
   until the meat is tender and the beans
   are cooked. Add a little water after an
   hour if necessary.
10. Serve with potatoes, rice or noodles.

Spaghetti alla Carbonara

Serves 4

Parma ham is air-dried Italian ham, available from delicatessens. No salt is required in this
recipe, because the ham provides enough. This delicious and nourishing dish is cheap and
quick to make. The ham can be left out for a vegetarian meal.

½ lb (225g) spaghetti
1 clove garlic, minced (optional)
1 dessertspoon (12ml) olive oil
4 eggs
2 tablespoons (36ml) fresh parsley, chopped
1½ oz (45g) hard sheep's or goat's milk cheese, finely grated
2 oz (55g) Parma ham (or 2 slices), chopped

1. Put a large pan of water on to boil for the spaghetti.
2. In a saucepan, sauté the garlic clove, if using, in the olive oil over a low heat.
3. Start cooking the spaghetti.
4. Trim the fat off the ham and slice the meat into small strips.
5. In a mixing bowl, whisk together the eggs, parsley and cheese.
6. Pour the eggs into the saucepan with the olive oil in it and scramble. Stir in the chopped ham.
7. When the spaghetti is cooked, drain it and stir it into the eggs.
8. Serve with a green salad.

Spicy Chicken and Yogurt _____E

Serves 3 or more

Try 2 tablespoons (36ml) chopped fresh mint instead of the curry powder for a different flavour.

6 chicken thighs
1×9 oz (250g) carton sheep's or goat's milk yogurt
1 teaspoon (6ml) cornflour
1 garlic clove, crushed
1 dessertspoon (12ml) mild Madras curry powder, or to taste
Sea salt and freshly ground black pepper

1. Remove the skin from the chicken thighs and slash each 2 or 3 times.
2. Make a paste with a teaspoon of yogurt and the cornflour. Stir this mixture into the rest of the yogurt.
3. Combine the yogurt, crushed garlic clove, curry powder and seasoning.
4. Marinate the meat for an hour before cooking, or less, if time is limited.
5. Preheat the grill.
6. Place the chicken thighs on the grill pan rack, and spoon some of the remaining marinade on top.
7. Grill for 25–30 minutes, turning once. The meat is done when the juice runs clear after a skewer has been inserted.
8. Serve with rice.

Turkey and Broccoli Bake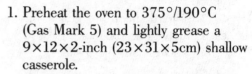E

Serves 6

This is a good way to use up turkey after Christmas. It is equally delicious when made with chicken, in which case it would require about half the meat from an average roast chicken.

10 oz (285g) broccoli
9 oz (225g) cooked turkey
3 oz (85g) Feta cheese
4 oz (115g) mushrooms, sliced
Oil, for frying
2 oz (55g) margarine
2 oz (55g) flour
½ teaspoon (3ml) dry mustard
1¼ pints (710ml) goat's or sheep's milk or
   unsweetened soya milk
Sea salt and freshly ground black pepper
3 oz (85g) homemade dried breadcrumbs

1. Preheat the oven to 375°/190°C (Gas Mark 5) and lightly grease a 9×12×2-inch (23×31×5cm) shallow casserole.
2. Cut the broccoli into florets and slice the stems into pieces of similar size. Cook it until it is barely tender.
3. Shred the turkey into strips, and grate the cheese in a handgrater. Reserve.
4. Sauté the sliced mushrooms in a little oil.
5. Melt the margarine in a saucepan, stir in the flour and mustard, and whisk in the milk. Cook over a medium low heat, stirring all the time, until the sauce boils and thickens.
6. Add the seasoning and the grated cheese to the sauce. Stir.
7. Distribute the cooked broccoli all over the base of the casserole.
8. Spread the turkey and mushrooms over the broccoli.
9. Cover with the cheese sauce.
10. Top with the dried breadcrumbs.
11. Bake for about 30 minutes, or until the breadcrumbs are golden and the sauce is bubbling.

Chicken Stir-fry _____ E W

Serves 4

Be sure to use olive oil, as it contributes a great deal to the flavour of this quickly prepared meal.

¾ lb (340g) raw chicken pieces
½ onion, chopped
Olive oil, for frying
½ green pepper, thinly sliced
1 head of broccoli
4 oz (115g) mushrooms, sliced
Sea salt and freshly ground black pepper

1. Skin the chicken pieces, bone them, and cut the meat into thin strips.
2. Sauté the chopped onion in olive oil in a large non-stick frying pan, until it is transparent.
3. Add the chicken and other vegetables and cook for about 10–15 minutes, tossing frequently, until the vegetables are barely tender and the chicken has turned white. Season to taste.
4. Serve with rice or noodles.

Chicken Orange Salad _____ W

Serves 6

This can be an egg-free dish if more yogurt is substituted for the mayonnaise.

1 oz (30g) blanched, slivered almonds (optional)
1 lb (455g) cooked chicken
4 tablespoons (72ml) mayonnaise
4 tablespoons (72ml) sheep's or goat's milk yogurt
2 oranges
A few lettuce leaves
Watercress, to garnish

1. Toast the slivered almonds (if using) under the grill and reserve.
2. Remove the skin and bones from the chicken and cut the meat into strips.
3. Put the mayonnaise and yogurt in a bowl and stir in the chicken.
4. Peel the oranges over the bowl, allowing the juice to drip into the chicken mixture.
5. Separate the peeled oranges into segments and cut each segment in half. Stir the orange pieces into the chicken mixture, cover and chill.
6. Serve on a bed of lettuce garnished with the toasted almonds (if used) and a few sprigs of watercress.

American Chicken Salad_____W

Serves 3

To make this salad egg-free, substitute more yogurt for the mayonnaise. This is a good way to use up left-over chicken.

½ lb (225g) cooked chicken
1 stick celery
2 oz (55g) mayonnaise
2 oz (55g) sheep's or goat's milk yogurt
Sea salt and freshly ground black pepper
A few lettuce leaves
Fresh parsley, chopped to garnish

1. Remove the skin and bones from the chicken and chop the meat into cubes.
2. Finely chop the celery.
3. In a bowl, mix together the mayonnaise, yogurt, chicken and celery. Season.
4. Serve on a bed of lettuce, topped with parsley. This is also delicious with lettuce in a sandwich.

Roquefort Meatloaf_____E W

Serves 4

Serve cold with watercress around the sides, accompanied by salads. This is a rich meatloaf, so it is best sliced not too thickly.

1 lb (455g) lean minced beef
2 oz (55g) Roquefort cheese, crumbled
1 dessertspoon (12ml) Worcester sauce
Watercress, for garnish

1. Preheat the oven to 350°F/180°C (Gas Mark 4), and grease a 1 lb (455g) loaf tin.
2. Mix all the ingredients together thoroughly.
3. Bake, covered, in the tin for 1 hour.
4. Remove the loaf from the oven, drain off the fat, loosen the edges and let it cool before turning it out. *Freeze at this point if desired.*
5. Serve cold with watercress around the sides, accompanied by salads.

VEGETARIAN MAIN COURSES

This chapter concentrates on dishes made from beans, vegetables, sheep's or goat's milk products, bread and eggs. The recipes are divided into groups: beans, Italian dishes, cheese and eggs, and quiches.

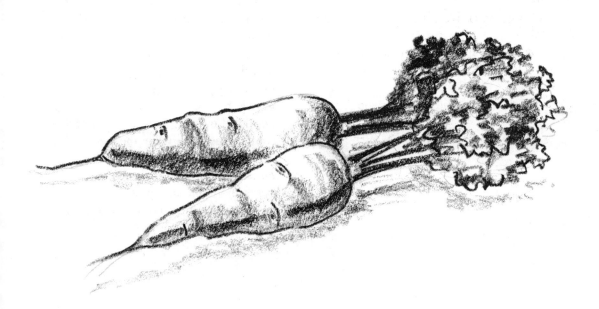

BEANS
Chilli E W

Serves 4–5

In addition to yogurt and cheese, chilli is also delicious served with Guacamole (see the recipe on page 32).

½ lb (225g) dried kidney beans, soaked overnight
½ lb (225g) rice
1 onion, chopped
1 clove garlic, minced
½ green pepper, chopped
Oil, for frying
2×14 oz (395g) tins tomatoes
6 tablespoons (108ml) concentrated tomato purée
¼-½ teaspoon (1.5-3ml) chilli powder, or to taste
Sea salt and freshly ground black pepper
Small bowlful of sheep's or goat's milk yogurt
2 oz (55g) Feta cheese, finely grated

1. Rinse the soaked kidney beans and put them in a pan of cold water. Bring the beans to the boil, boil them rapidly for 10 minutes, then simmer for 40 minutes.
2. Meanwhile put a pan of salted water on to boil, then add the rice.
3. Sauté the onion, garlic and green pepper in a little oil. (At this point ½ lb (225g) of lean minced beef or lamb can be added and browned, if desired.)
4. Chop the tinned tomatoes roughly and add them to the other ingredients in the frying pan, along with the cooked kidney beans, tomato purée and chilli powder. Cover, bring to the boil and simmer the chilli while the rice cooks, about 20 minutes. Season to taste. *Freeze at this point if desired.*
5. Serve the chilli on top of the rice, accompanied by a bowl of yogurt and the grated Feta.

TVP and Vegetable Crumble _____ E W

Serves 5–6

The strong taste of the TVP is completely altered by the flavours of the other ingredients.
4 oz (115g) steamed French beans, cut into bite-sized pieces, can be substituted for the swede
or turnip. If you don't have the fresh herbs, substitute 2 teaspoons (36ml) Italian seasoning.

For the casserole:

1 onion, chopped
2 sticks celery, chopped
4 oz (115g) swede or turnip, scraped and
  cubed
Oil, for frying
15 fl oz (425ml) stock made with
  1 teaspoon (6ml) yeast extract
4 oz (115g) TVP mince
2×14 oz (395g) tins tomatoes
4 tablespoons (60ml) tomato purée
6 oz (170g) carrots, scrubbed and grated
2 teaspoons (10ml) fresh thyme, chopped
1 teaspoon (5ml) fresh oregano, chopped
1 teaspoon (5ml) fresh basil, chopped
1 dried bay leaf
Sea salt and freshly ground black pepper

For the crumble topping:

2 oz (55g) Feta cheese, finely grated
2 oz (55g) porridge oats
1 oz (30g) margarine

1. Preheat the oven to 350°F/180°C
   (Gas Mark 4). Lightly grease a 3½-pint
   (2 litre) casserole.

2. In a large non-stick frying pan, sauté
   the onion, celery and swede or turnip
   in the oil.

3. Stir the stock into the TVP until all of it
   has been absorbed, then add it to the
   contents of the frying pan. Roughly
   chop the tomatoes and stir them into
   the mixture, along with the tomato
   purée, grated carrots, herbs and
   seasoning.

4. Pour the TVP and vegetable mix into
   the prepared casserole. In a bowl rub
   the crumble ingredients together, then
   distribute them evenly on top.

5. Bake for about 40 minutes, or until
   brown and bubbling.

Sweet and Sour Tofu _____ E W

Serves 4

Although this recipe looks long, it is actually very quick to prepare. If you want a meal that is practically instant, substitute a 10 oz (285g) tin mixed Chinese vegetables for the bamboo shoots, fresh beansprouts and carrot.

1 onion, chopped
1 oz (30g) green pepper, chopped small (optional)
Oil, for frying
4 oz (115g) tofu
2 tablespoons (36ml) soy sauce
1×14 oz (395g) tin tomatoes
1×8 oz (225g) tin bamboo shoots
4 oz (115g) fresh beansprouts
1 carrot, grated
2 tablespoons (36ml) Muscovado sugar
2 tablespoons (36ml) wine vinegar
2 tablespoons (36ml) cornflour

1. Sauté the onion and green pepper (if using) in a little oil in a large non-stick frying pan.
2. Mince the tofu (this is best done in a food processor fitted with the metal blade).
3. Add the tofu and soy sauce to the frying pan, and brown the tofu on a medium-high heat.
4. Chop the tomatoes roughly inside the tin and pour them into the frying pan.
5. Drain the bamboo shoots and stir them into the other ingredients.
6. Put the beansprouts in a bowl and pour boiling water on them. Wait for 15 seconds, drain, and add them to the sauce, then add the carrot.
7. In a cup, mix together the Muscovado sugar, wine vinegar and cornflour, and pour the paste into the sauce.
8. Bring to the boil, then simmer for 20 minutes, stirring occasionally.
9. Serve on a bed of rice or Chinese noodles.

Tofu Fried Rice _____ E W

Serves 3 or 4

This is a basic recipe to which strips of left-over chicken, cooked shrimps, cockles, peas and/or 1 or 2 eggs can be stirred in along with the beansprouts and spring onions. Try to buy additive-free soy sauce.

½ lb (225g) rice, weighed before cooking
4 oz (115g) tofu, drained
2 tablespoons (36ml) oil
2 tablespoons (36ml) soy sauce, or more, to taste
4 oz (115g) fresh beansprouts, or 1×10 oz (285g) tin, drained
4 spring onions, chopped, including the green parts
Sea salt and freshly ground black pepper

1. Cook the rice, drain and rinse it.
2. Mince the tofu (this is best done in a food processor fitted with the metal blade).
3. Heat the oil in a large non-stick frying pan or wok and add the tofu and soy sauce. Cook until the tofu is browned.
4. Put the fresh beansprouts in a bowl and cover them with boiling water. Wait 15 seconds, then drain them. (Leave this step out if you are using tinned beansprouts.)
5. Add the cooked rice to the frying pan and stir-fry the rice and tofu over a medium heat.
6. Stir in the beansprouts and spring onions and continue to cook, tossing frequently, for about 5 minutes. Season.
7. This will serve 3 people on its own, or 4 with vegetables on the side.

ITALIAN DISHES
Bolognese Sauce _____ E W

Serves 4

This is a basic recipe which is used again in the following dishes. When serving Bolognese Sauce on spaghetti, macaroni or risotto, you can add some calcium by passing a bowl of finely grated hard sheep's or goat's milk cheese. Various additions can be made. For example, 4 oz (115g) sliced mushrooms can be browned along with the onion and garlic, 2 oz (55g) TVP mince mixed with 4 fl oz (90ml) water can be stirred in, and 2 oz (55g) sliced carrots can be cooked and added to the sauce.

1 onion, chopped
1 clove garlic, minced
Olive oil, for frying
2×14 oz (390g) tins tomatoes
6 tablespoons (108ml) concentrated tomato purée
2 teaspoons (12ml) oregano, chopped fresh or dried
1 teaspoon (6ml) thyme, chopped fresh or dried
Sea salt and freshly ground black pepper

1. In a large non-stick frying pan with a lid, sauté the onion and garlic in olive oil.
2. Roughly chop the tinned tomatoes and add them to the pan with their juice.
3. Stir in the tomato purée, herbs and seasoning.
4. Bring the sauce to the boil, then simmer for 20 minutes. *Freeze at this point if desired.*
5. Serve on pasta.

Pizza _____ E

Makes 5 Pizzas

For the dough:

1 lb (455g) flour
1 sachet dried yeast
1½ teaspoons (9ml) salt
½ pint (285ml) warm water
2 tablespoons (36ml) olive oil

1. Put the flour in a mixing bowl and stir in the dried yeast.
2. Dissolve the salt in the warm water.
3. Make a well in the centre of the flour and gradually pour in the water, mixing it with one hand.
4. When the mixture is elastic and of a

For the basic topping:

1 quantity Bolognese Sauce
 (see opposite)
6 oz (170g) Feta cheese, coarsely
 grated

For the variations:

A few ounces fresh whitebait
Anchovies, tinned
Mussels or clams, tinned
Italian sausage, sliced
Olives
Spring onions, sliced
Onion rings
Red or green pepper, sliced, lightly fried in
 olive oil
Mushrooms, sliced

uniform consistency, put it in a bowl
and cover it with a towel. Put it in a
warm place to prove for about an hour,
or until it has doubled in size.

5. Put the dough on a floured surface
 and knead it well. Gradually
 incorporate the olive oil.
6. Oil five 8½-inch (22cm) round
 aluminium flan cases.
7. Divide the dough into 5 portions, then
 work each into a flat, round shape. Put
 each round into a flan case, pressing it
 right up to the rim with your fingers.
8. Leave them for 20 minutes to prove.
9. Divide the Bolognese Sauce equally
 among the pizzas, then do the same
 with the grated cheese. *Freeze at this
 point if desired.*
10. To bake the pizzas, preheat the oven to
 425°F/220°C (Gas Mark 7).
11. Add one or more of the variations to
 the basic pizza, then put them in the
 oven for 15 minutes.
12. Reduce the heat to 375°F/190°C
 (Gas Mark 5), and bake for a further
 5-10 minutes.
13. Serve with a salad.

Pastitsio

Serves 5-6

This recipe is fast to make, and is the sort of dish you can fall back on when you think there is nothing in the house to eat!

Sea salt
½ lb (225g) thick macaroni
1 quantity Bolognese Sauce (see page 90)
1 oz (30g) breadcrumbs
2 oz (55g) Feta cheese, coarsely grated

1. Preheat the oven to 375°F/190°C (Gas Mark 5).
2. Heat a large pan of salted water. When it has boiled add the macaroni and cook for about 9 minutes, until it is just tender.
3. Combine the drained macaroni and Bolognese Sauce in a 2½-3-pint (1.4-1.7 litre) casserole.
4. Top with the breadcrumbs and cheese.
6. Bake, uncovered, for 20-30 minutes.
7. Serve with a green salad.

Italian Courgettes   E

Serves 4

1 lb (455g) courgettes
Sea salt
1 quantity Bolognese Sauce (see page 90)
1 oz (30g) breadcrumbs, dried
3 oz (85g) Feta cheese, coarsely grated

1. Preheat the oven to 375°F/190°C (Gas Mark 5).
2. Rinse and slice the courgettes crosswise, then cook them with a little salt until just tender.
3. In a shallow 8×12-inch (20×25cm) casserole, spread ⅓ of the Bolognese Sauce, then layer the courgettes on top. Cover with the remaining sauce.
4. Arrange the breadcrumbs on the sauce, then sprinkle on the grated cheese.

5. Bake for 25–30 minutes.
6. Serve with pasta, rice or a baked potato.

Mushroom Risotto   E W

Serves 3–4

For the risotto:

½ onion, chopped
1 clove garlic, minced
1 tablespoon (18ml) olive oil
½ lb (225g) mushrooms, sliced
1 pint (570ml) vegetable stock, made from
  a cube
½ lb (225g) Italian rice, uncooked
Freshly ground black pepper
1 tablespoon (18ml) fresh parsley, chopped

For the Bolognese Sauce:

½ onion, chopped
1 clove garlic, minced
Oil, for frying
1×14 oz (295g) tin tomatoes
3 tablespoons (54ml) concentrated tomato
  purée
1 teaspoon (6ml) fresh thyme, chopped
1½ teaspoons (7.5ml) fresh oregano,
  chopped
Sea salt and freshly ground black pepper

For the 'Parmesan' cheese:

2 oz (55g) hard sheep's or goat's milk
  cheese, finely grated

1. Start the risotto in a large non-stick frying pan with a lid. Sauté the onion and garlic in the olive oil, then add the mushrooms. Add the vegetable stock and rice, and bring the risotto to the boil. Season with pepper and simmer for 20–30 minutes, or until all the liquid is absorbed and the rice is cooked. Stir in the parsley.
2. Meanwhile make the Bolognese Sauce in a small non-stick frying pan. Sauté the onion and garlic in the oil over a low heat. Chop the tomatoes roughly and add them to the pan along with the tomato purée, herbs and seasoning.
3. Bring the Bolognese Sauce to the boil and simmer it while the risotto finishes cooking.
4. Serve the risotto with the Bolognese Sauce poured over it. Pass around the grated cheese for people to help themselves.

Pasta Primavera

Serves 4

This is quick, delicious and nutritious. You could try substituting other vegetables in season.

½ lb (225g) spaghetti, noodles or linguine
2 tablespoons (36ml) olive oil
1 onion, chopped
1 clove garlic, minced
4 oz (115g) button mushrooms, sliced
4 oz (115g) carrots, cut into slivers
4 oz (115g) broccoli or calabrese, cut into florets with stems slivered
4 oz (115g) cauliflower, cut into small florets
4 oz (115g) courgettes, sliced
Sea salt and freshly ground black pepper
3 spring onions, sliced
1 tablespoon (18ml) fresh basil or parsley, chopped
2 oz (55g) hard goat's or sheep's milk cheese, finely grated

1. Put a large saucepan of salted water on to boil for the pasta.
2. In a large non-stick frying pan or wok, heat the olive oil and sauté the onion and garlic until transparent. Add the mushrooms and cook for a few more minutes.
4. When the water has boiled and the pasta is cooking, start to stir-fry the carrots, broccoli, cauliflower and courgettes. Season.
5. During the last two minutes while the pasta is finishing cooking, add the spring onions to the stir-fry.
6. Just before serving, add the basil or parsley. Arrange the vegetables on top of the pasta, and pass the grated cheese at the table.

CHEESE AND EGGS

Cheese and Herb Omelette _____ W

Serves 4

6 eggs
6 fl oz (170ml) goat's or sheep's milk or
  unsweetened soya milk
1 tablespoon (18ml) fresh chives, chopped
1 teaspoon (6ml) fresh parsley, chopped
½ teaspoon (3ml) fresh dill, chopped
Sea salt and freshly ground black pepper
Oil, for frying
2 oz (55g) Feta cheese, finely grated

1. Mix together all the ingredients except
   the oil and cheese.
2. Heat the oil in a large non-stick frying
   pan and pour in the egg mixture.
3. Over a medium heat, push the
   uncooked eggs on the edges towards
   the centre until the omelette is
   beginning to set, then sprinkle the
   grated cheese on top and let it melt.
4. Fold the omelette in half, cook for a
   minute or two more, then slide it onto
   a warmed platter.

Broccoli and Cheese Pancakes

Serves 4

Pancakes can be made ahead, separated by pieces of greaseproof paper, and then frozen. Yorkshire puddings can also be made with goat's or sheep's milk or unsweetened soya milk instead of cow's milk, with no detectable difference in texture or taste.

For the pancake batter:

4 oz (115g) flour
Pinch of salt
1 egg, beaten
½ pint (285ml) goat's or sheep's milk or
   unsweetened soya milk
Oil, for frying

For the filling:

1 oz (30g) margarine
1 oz (30g) flour
1 teaspoon (6ml) dry English mustard
½ pint (285ml) goat's or sheep's milk or
   unsweetened soya milk
4 oz (115g) Feta cheese, finely grated
Freshly ground black pepper
1 lb (455g) broccoli or calabrese, trimmed
   and cut into florets

1. Allow at least half an hour for the batter to stand before making the pancakes. Put the flour and salt in a bowl and make a well in the centre. Beat the egg into the flour, then gradually beat in the goat's or soya milk.

2. In a saucepan, melt the margarine, then stir in the flour and mustard. Pour in the goat's or soya milk, whisking all the time over a medium heat until the sauce is thickened.

3. Take the white sauce off the heat, and stir in the grated cheese until it melts. Season with pepper.

4. Fry 8 pancakes in oil, keeping each one warm in the oven while the next one cooks.

5. Meanwhile cook the broccoli until just tender.

6. To assemble, divide the broccoli among the pancakes, roll them up, and pour the heated cheese sauce over.

7. Serve two filled pancakes per person on heated plates.

Cheese and Broccoli Baked Potatoes___E W

Serves 4

4 oz (115g) leeks can be used in place of the broccoli.

4 potatoes, baked
4 oz (115g) broccoli or calabrese, chopped
Pinch of sea salt
4 oz (115g) Feta cheese, finely grated
¼ pint (425ml) sheep's or goat's milk
  yogurt
Soft margarine, to taste (optional)
Freshly ground black pepper

1. Bake the potatoes in the usual way, for about an hour in a moderate oven.
2. Steam the chopped broccoli with salt until just tender.
3. Mix together the cheese, yogurt and cooked broccoli.
4. Remove the potatoes from the oven. Slit each down the middle and mash the flesh with a fork. The margarine, if used, can be mixed in at this point.
5. Stuff the potatoes with the cheese and broccoli mix, season to taste and return them to the oven. Bake for a further 10–15 minutes.

Leek Piperade

Serves 4

This dish is suitable for brunch, lunch or supper.

1 quantity leeks niçoise (see point 1)
6 eggs
3 fl oz (90ml) goat's or sheep's milk or
  unsweetened soya milk
Sea salt and freshly ground black pepper
½ oz (15g) margarine
4 slices bread, toasted
1½ tablespoons fresh parsley or chives,
  chopped

1. Make the leeks niçoise as on page 109, omitting the cheese. Keep them warm on a low heat.
2. Beat together the eggs, milk and seasoning.
3. Melt the margarine in a saucepan, pour in the egg mixture, and scramble.
4. Make the toast.
5. Layer each slice of toast with leeks niçoise and eggs. Serve with a sprinkling of parsley or chives on top of each portion.

Cheese Soufflé

Serves 4

4 tablespoons (72ml) dried breadcrumbs
1 oz (30g) margarine
1 onion, chopped
½ oz (15g) flour
1 teaspoon (6ml) French mustard
½ pint (285ml) goat's or sheep's milk or
    unsweetened soya milk
4 oz (115g) Feta cheese, finely grated
3 eggs, separated
Sea salt and freshly ground black pepper

1. Preheat the oven to 350°F/180°C (Gas Mark 4), and grease a 2-pint (1.1 litre) soufflé dish. Sprinkle on the dried breadcrumbs.
2. In a small non-stick frying pan, melt the margarine and sauté the onion until transparent.
3. Stir in the flour and mustard and cook for a minute or two. Still stirring, pour the milk in gradually, and bring the sauce to the boil over a medium heat.
4. Remove the sauce from the heat, then mix in the finely grated cheese until it dissolves.
5. Separate the eggs and whisk the whites until stiff. Beat the yolks and stir them into the sauce, then fold the egg whites into the sauce with a metal spoon.
6. Pour the mixture into the soufflé dish and bake for 45–50 minutes, or until the soufflé is risen and golden.
7. Serve immediately.

QUICHES

Quiches are rich in calcium, with their combination of eggs, milk, cheese and flour. When the vegetable in the filling provides a generous amount of calcium, for example in the case of Broccoli Quiche (page 100), then so much the better. If you are using Trex vegetable shortening for the pastry, you will need 3½ oz (100g) flour and 1½ oz (45g) Trex for an 8-inch (20.5cm) quiche dish, and 5oz (140g) flour, 3 oz (85g) Trex for a 10-inch (25.5cm) one. Rub in and roll out the pastry in the usual way and fill the quiche dish with it. To bake it blind, put a sheet of greaseproof paper weighed down with dried beans inside the pastry case and bake at 425°F/220°C (Gas Mark 7) for 7 minutes. Remove the paper and the beans and bake for a further 7 minutes.

Filled quiches can be frozen, but I prefer to freeze the unbaked pastry cases. Having some frozen ones on hand is a great time-saver if you are in a hurry. All of the following quiches contain eggs, but there is one egg-free quiche recipe in the fish chapter: Tuna and Cucumber Quiche on page 64.

Leek Quiche

Serves 6

1 × 8-inch (20.5cm) pastry case, baked blind (see note, above)
1 onion, chopped
1 lb (455g) leeks, sliced
Oil, for frying
2 eggs
5 fl oz goat's or sheep's milk or unsweetened soya milk
3 oz (55g) Feta cheese, finely grated
Sea salt and freshly ground black pepper

1. Bake the pastry case blind.
2. Keep the oven set at 425°F/220°C (Gas Mark 7).
3. Sauté the onion and leeks in the minimum of oil in a large non-stick frying pan.
4. Whisk the eggs, adding the goat's, sheep's or soya milk and seasoning.
5. Put the leeks and onions in the bottom of the pastry case and distribute the cheese evenly on top. Pour in the egg custard.
6. Bake for 10 minutes at 425°F/220°C (Gas Mark 7), then at 375°F/190°C (Gas Mark 5) for about 25 minutes, or until the quiche is golden and set.
7. Serve hot or cold.

Mushroom Quiche

Serves 8

1×10-inch (25.5cm) pastry case, baked
  blind (see note, on page 99)
1 medium onion, chopped
Oil, for frying
9 oz (255g) mushrooms, sliced
1 teaspoon (6ml) lemon juice
2 tablespoons (36ml) fresh parsley,
  chopped
4 eggs
½ pint (285ml) goat's or sheep's milk or
  unsweetened soya milk
Sea salt and freshly ground black pepper
4 oz (115g) Feta cheese, finely grated

1. Bake the pastry case blind.
2. Keep the oven set at 425°F/220°C
   (Gas Mark 7).
3. In a large non-stick frying pan, sauté
   the onion in a small amount of oil,
   then add the mushrooms and cook
   them until soft.
4. Sprinkle the lemon juice over the
   mushrooms, then stir in the parsley.
5. Beat the eggs and milk together and
   season.
6. To assemble the quiche, put the onions
   and mushrooms in the bottom of the
   pastry case, then spread the cheese
   evenly on top. Pour in the egg custard.
7. Bake at 425°F/220°C (Gas Mark 7)
   for 15 minutes, then at 375°F/190°C
   (Gas Mark 5) for about 20 minutes, or
   until the quiche is golden and set.
9. Serve hot or cold.

Broccoli Quiche

Serves 6

6 oz (170g) chopped asparagus can be substituted for the broccoli.

1 × 8-inch (20.5cm) pastry case, baked
  blind (see note, on page 99)
6 oz (170g) broccoli or calabrese
Sea salt
½ onion, chopped
Oil, for frying
2 eggs
5 fl oz (140ml) goat's or sheep's milk or
  unsweetened soya milk
Freshly ground black pepper
4 oz (115g) Feta cheese, finely grated

1. Bake the pastry case blind.
2. Keep the oven set at 425°F/220°C
   (Gas Mark 7).
3. Chop the broccoli into ½-inch (1cm)
   pieces and cook in a little salted water
   until just tender.
4. In a small non-stick frying pan, sauté
   the onion in a small amount of oil over
   a low heat.
5. Beat together the eggs and milk and
   add the pepper.
6. Put the cooked broccoli and onion in
   the pastry case, then sprinkle the
   cheese evenly on top. Pour in the egg
   custard.
7. Bake for 15 minutes at the original
   oven setting, then for about 20 minutes
   at 375°F/190°C (Gas Mark 5).
8. Serve hot or cold.

Roquefort Quiche

Serves 6

1 × 8-inch (20.5cm) pastry case, baked
  blind (see note, on page 99)
½ onion, chopped
Oil, for frying
2 eggs
5 fl oz (140ml) goat's or sheep's milk or
  unsweetened soya milk
2 oz (55g) Roquefort or Lanark Blue
  cheese, finely grated
4 oz (155g) Feta cheese, finely grated

1. Bake the pastry case blind.
2. Keep the oven at 425°F/220°C
   (Gas Mark 7).
3. Sauté the onion in the minimum of oil
   in a small non-stick frying pan.
4. Beat together the eggs and milk.
5. Scatter the onion on the base of the
   pastry case and spread the grated
   cheese on top. Pour the egg custard
   over the cheese.
6. Bake for about 30 minutes at
   425°F/220°C (Gas Mark 7), or until
   golden and set.
7. Serve hot or cold.

Spinach Quiche

Serves 6

Double the filling ingredients for a 10-inch (25.5cm) quiche.

1×8-inch (20.5cm) pastry case, baked
  blind (see note on page 99)
½ lb (225g) spinach, fresh or frozen
Sea salt
2 eggs
4 fl oz (120ml) goat's or sheep's milk or
  unsweetened soya milk
4 oz (115g) Feta cheese, finely grated

1. Bake the pastry case blind.
2. Keep the oven set at 425°F/220°C
   (Gas Mark 7).
3. Cook the spinach in a little salted
   water, then drain it, squeezing out the
   excess liquid.
4. In a food processor fitted with the
   metal blade, mix the spinach, eggs,
   milk and grated cheese until the
   texture is uniform. Alternatively, beat
   the eggs, milk and cheese together,
   then chop the spinach, and stir it into
   the egg mixture.
5. Pour the filling into the pastry case.
6. Bake for 15 minutes at the original
   oven setting, then for 20 minutes at
   375°F/190°C (Gas Mark 5).

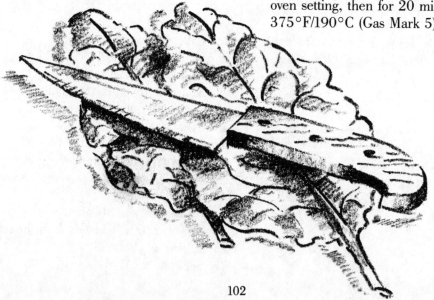

VEGETABLES

On a milk-exclusion diet you should be eating dark green leafy vegetables, beans, pulses, and root vegetables more often. One of my favourite vegetables is plain cooked broccoli, which blends well with most foods. The recipes in this chapter are for vegetables prepared with sauces or an unusual combination of flavours, which can add interest to a plain meal such as grilled meat or fish. Some of the recipes are substantial enough for a main course. For example, Courgette Bake, Cauliflower au Gratin, Ratatouille, and Stir-fry Vegetables can all serve as the basis of a vegetarian meal.

Broad Beans in Parsley Sauce _____ E

Serves 4-5

As the broad bean season is so short, you may wish to use 1 lb (455g) frozen beans when fresh beans are unavailable.

3-4 lb (1½-2kg) fresh broad beans
1 oz (30g) margarine
1 oz (30g) flour
1 teaspoon (6ml) dry mustard
½ pint (285ml) goat's or sheep's milk or unsweetened soya milk
Sea salt and freshly ground black pepper
1 oz (30g) fresh parsley, chopped

1. Shell the broad beans and cook them until they are tender.
2. Meanwhile melt the margarine in a saucepan and stir in the flour and mustard. Whisk in the goat's, sheep's or soya milk, and cook the sauce over a medium-low heat until it boils and thickens, stirring all the time. Season.
3. Add the chopped parsley to the sauce.
4. Put the cooked beans in a shallow bowl, pour the parsley sauce on top and serve.

Boston Baked Beans _____E W

Serves 12

This is perfect for feeding a large crowd at a barbecue.

1 lb (455g) haricot beans, soaked
overnight
4 oz (115g) salt pork or green bacon joint
2 tablespoons (36ml) black strap molasses
(i.e., pure cane)
2 tablespoons (36ml) concentrated tomato
purée
2 dessertspoons (24ml) dry English
mustard
1 teaspoon (6ml) salt
Freshly ground black pepper
1 onion, peeled

1. Preheat the oven to 325°F/170°C
   (Gas Mark 3).
2. Drain and rinse the beans, and put
   them in a large saucepan. Pour enough
   water on to the beans to cover them,
   plus an extra inch (2.5cm).
3. Bring the beans to the boil, then
   simmer them for 1 hour. Drain,
   reserving 1¼ pints (710ml) of the
   liquid.
4. Cut the salt pork or bacon joint in two
   pieces and place one half at the bottom
   of a 6-pint (3.4 litre) casserole with a
   lid. Slice the other half into 4 or 5
   pieces for placing on top of the beans
   later.
5. Mix together the molasses, tomato
   purée, mustard and salt, and combine
   with the bean cooking liquid.
6. Layer half the beans in the casserole
   and cover with half of the molasses
   mixture. Season with pepper. Repeat.
7. Nestle the whole onion in the beans,
   dot with the salt pork or bacon, and
   cover.
8. Bake for 2 hours, or until the beans
   are tender. Then add a little more
   liquid and remove the cover. Bake for
   1 more hour, in order to brown the
   top.

Cauliflower au Gratin _____ E

Serves 4

If you are cooking a large cauliflower, double the ingredients for the sauce. This recipe can be used for 1 lb (455g) sliced leeks or ¼ cabbage, shredded. It can also be made with 1 lb (455g) broccoli, leaving out the nutmeg.

1 small cauliflower
Sea salt
1 oz (30g) margarine
½ oz (15g) flour
½ pint (285ml) goat's or sheep's milk or
  sugarless soya milk
Dash of nutmeg
Freshly ground black pepper
2 oz (55g) dried homemade breadcrumbs
2 oz (55g) Feta cheese, finely grated

1. Preheat the oven to 375°F/190°C (Gas Mark 5).
2. Break the cauliflower into florets and cook it with a little salt until it is just becoming tender.
3. Melt the margarine in a saucepan, stir in the flour and then the milk. Gradually bring the sauce to the boil, stirring all the time. When it has thickened add the nutmeg and pepper.
4. Put the cauliflower in a shallow 1½-pint (850ml) casserole, and distribute the breadcrumbs and grated cheese over the top.
5. Bake for 15–20 minutes and serve.

Tasty Cabbage _____ E W

Serves 4

¾ lb (340g) cabbage, roughly shredded
½ onion, chopped
1¼ pints (710ml) water
½ chicken stock cube or 1 teaspoon (6ml)
  yeast extract
Freshly ground black pepper

1. Prepare the vegetables and put the water on to boil in a large saucepan.
2. Crumble the stock cube in the water or stir in the yeast extract.
3. Put the cabbage and onion into the boiling water and cook until tender.
4. Drain and put the cabbage in a bowl. Season with pepper and serve.

Carrot and Parsnip Purée _____ E W

Serves 4

This is very filling, and can be served in place of potatoes.

10 oz (285g) parsnips
6 oz (170g) carrots
3 tablespoons (54ml) goat's or sheep's milk
or unsweetened soya milk
Dash of nutmeg
Sea salt and freshly ground black pepper
1 tablespoon (18ml) fresh parsley, chopped

1. Scrub the vegetables, slice them, and cook until tender.
2. Transfer the vegetables to a bowl, and mash or whip them.
3. Stir in enough milk to make the dish the consistency of mashed potatoes.
4. Stir in the nutmeg, seasoning and parsley. Serve.

Carrots Baked in Orange Juice _____ E W

Serves 4

These carrots can be cooked in the oven along with other food at a lower temperature.

1 lb (455g) carrots
Juice of 1 orange

1. Preheat the oven to 400°F/200°C (Gas Mark 6).
2. Scrub the carrots, cut them into julienne strips and put them in a shallow casserole with a lid.
3. Pour the orange juice over them.
4. Bake, covered, for 30 minutes.

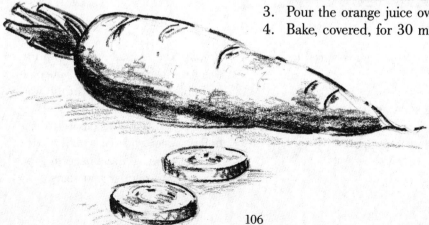

Braised Celery _____ E

Serves 4

½ lb (225g) celery
1 oz (30g) margarine
1 dessertspoon (12ml) flour
¼ pint (140ml) chicken stock made from
  ¼ stock cube
Sea salt and freshly ground black pepper

1. Preheat the oven to 425°F/220°C (Gas Mark 7).
2. Trim the celery and cut each stick in half. Slice thick pieces down the middle for a uniform effect.
3. In a non-stick frying pan, soften the celery in the margarine over a medium-low heat for about 5 minutes. Transfer the celery to a shallow 1½-pint (850ml) casserole with a lid.
4. Stir the flour into the remaining melted margarine in the frying pan, then gradually stir in the chicken stock. Thicken slightly over a medium heat, stirring constantly, and pour the sauce on top of the celery. Season.
5. Cover and cook in the oven for about 20 minutes. If it has to be cooked at a lower temperature with other things in the oven it will take longer.
6. Serve with grilled or roast meat.

Courgettes and Almonds _____ E W

Serves 6

1 lb (455g) courgettes, sliced
Sea salt
Oil, for frying
1 oz (30g) flaked almonds

1. Put the courgettes in the minimum of oil in a large, non-stick frying pan. Cook them over a medium heat until they are tender. Add the salt.
2. Meanwhile toast the almonds under the grill.
3. Serve the cooked courgettes in a shallow bowl with a scattering of toasted almonds on top.

Courgette Bake _____ E W

Serves 4

Sliced aubergines and green pepper can be substituted for the courgettes and red pepper. Remember to slice the aubergines, sprinkle them with salt and leave them in a colander for 20 minutes before beginning the recipe. Either way, this dish has an attractive array of bright colours, and an equally interesting taste.

1 clove garlic, minced
2 oz (55g) onion, sliced in rings
2 oz (55g) red pepper, sliced in rings
Olive oil, for frying
¾ lb (340g) courgettes, sliced
6 oz (170g) tomatoes, sliced
Sea salt and freshly ground black pepper
2 oz (55g) hard sheep's or goat's milk
    cheese, finely grated

1. Preheat the oven to 375°F/190°C (Gas Mark 5).
2. In a large non-stick frying pan, sauté the garlic, onion and pepper rings in a little olive oil.
3. Add the courgettes and sauté them until they are beginning to be tender, but still have plenty of bite.
4. In a 9-inch (23cm) quiche dish, arrange the courgettes, garlic, onions, and red pepper. Distribute the sliced tomatoes on top, and season with salt and pepper.
5. Bake for 10–15 minutes, then remove the dish from the oven and sprinkle the cheese on top. Return the courgette bake to the oven and leave it there for another 5 minutes, or until the cheese has melted.
6. Serve either as an accompaniment to grilled meat or fish, or as a light meal in itself, of 2–3 servings.

Leeks Niçoise _____ E W

Serves 4-5

If you are using this recipe for Leek Piperade (see page 97) omit the cheese and heat the leeks and tomato sauce quickly in a saucepan.

1 lb (455g) leeks, sliced
½ clove garlic, minced
½ onion, chopped
1×14 oz (395g) tin tomatoes
2 tablespoons (36ml) concentrated tomato
  purée
1 tablespoon (18ml) fresh parsley, chopped
Sea salt and freshly ground black pepper
1 oz (30g) Feta cheese, finely grated

1. Preheat the oven to 350°F/180°C (Gas Mark 4).
2. Prepare the leeks, garlic and onion, and parboil or steam them together until they are cooked.
3. In a small bowl, mix together the tinned tomatoes, roughly chopped, the tomato purée and the parsley. Stir in the leek mixture and season.
4. Put the leeks and tomato mixture in a shallow 1½-pint (850ml) casserole and top with the grated cheese.
5. Bake, uncovered, for about 30 minutes, or until the sauce is bubbling and the cheese has melted.

Parsnip and Watercress Purée _____ E W

Serves 4

This dish has a delicate medley of flavours and a pleasing colour.

1 lb parsnips, scrubbed and sliced
Sea salt
2 oz (55g) or ½ bunch watercress, rinsed
  and roughly chopped
Freshly ground black pepper
1 tablespoon (18ml) reserved vegetable
  stock, or more

1. Cook the parsnips in a little salted water.
2. During the last 3 or 4 minutes of the cooking time, add the watercress to the parsnips. Drain, reserving the stock.
3. Purée the vegetables in a food processor fitted with the metal blade, or sieve through a handgrater. Season and then moisten with a little of the vegetable stock.
4. Put in a bowl and serve immediately.

Baked Potato with Yogurt and Chives _____ E W

Serves 4

Some people may wish to have margarine mixed into their potato before filling it, but it is not really necessary.

4 baking potatoes
Sea salt and freshly ground black pepper
⅓ pint (190ml) sheep's or goat's milk
  yogurt
4 teaspoons (24ml) fresh chives, chopped

1. Bake the potatoes in the usual way, for 1 hour in a moderate oven.
2. Remove the potatoes from the oven and slit them open. Season.
3. Fill the potatoes, allowing 3 tablespoons of yogurt and 1 teaspoon of chopped chives for each one.

Root Vegetable Ratatouille _____ E W

Serves 5

If a thicker consistency is preferred, pour away some of the juice from the tinned tomatoes.

1 medium onion, chopped
1 clove garlic, minced
1 tablespoon (18ml) oil
1 stick celery, sliced
1 leek, sliced
2 carrots, sliced
1 large courgette, sliced
1×14 oz (395g) tin tomatoes
2 tablespoons (36ml) concentrated tomato
  purée
Sea salt and freshly ground black pepper

1. Sauté the onion and garlic in oil in a large non-stick frying pan with a lid.
2. Add the rest of the fresh vegetables and the courgette to the pan. Cook, stirring frequently, for about 15 minutes, or until the vegetables are tender, but still have bite.
3. Chop the tomatoes roughly inside the tin and add them to the ratatouille along with the tomato purée. Heat thoroughly, and allow the sauce to reduce slightly. Season to taste and serve.

Baked Swede _____ E W

Serves 4

This recipe works well at higher or lower temperatures if the swede has to be cooked along with other things in the oven. Adjust cooking times accordingly. Other root vegetables that can be baked in this way include:

    turnips, cubed,
    carrots, sliced thinly lengthwise,
    mixed celery and carrots,
    chopped

¾ lb (340g) swede
1 teaspoon (6ml) margarine
3 tablespoons (54ml) water
Sea salt and freshly ground black pepper

1. Preheat the oven to 350°F/180°C (Gas Mark 4).
2. Scrape and cube the swede, and put it in a casserole with a lid.
3. Dot the swede with margarine, and add the water, salt and pepper.
4. Bake for about 40 minutes and serve.

Stir-fry Vegetables _____ E W

In a wok or a large non-stick frying pan, heat a small amount of olive or vegetable oil. Cut whatever vegetables you like into strips, then cook them quickly, tossing frequently. Start with the vegetables that take the longest to cook and add the others in turn, finishing with those that cook the fastest. For example you could start off with carrots, then add some broccoli, followed by spring onions, mushrooms, frozen peas and finally beansprouts.

SALADS

The recipes in this chapter are side salads, followed by salad dressings. More substantial salads, as well as mousses and quiches, can be found in the fish, vegetarian and main course chapters.

Green Salad _____ E W

Lettuce crisps beautifully if it is put in a metal bowl or colander after washing. You can boost the calcium in a green salad by adding spring onions, chopped celery or courgettes, radishes, grated carrot and lots of chopped fresh parsley, watercress or mustard and cress. Serve it with one of the yogurt dressings or the Tahini Dressing on page 123.

Tomato Salad _____ E W

Serves 4

4 tomatoes
Freshly ground black pepper
French Dressing, to taste (see the recipe on page 122)
2 tablespoons (36ml) fresh parsley, chopped

1. Slice the tomatoes thinly and put them in slightly overlapping rows on a plate.
2. Liberally season with pepper and dribble French Dressing on top.
3. Sprinkle the parsley on the tomatoes and serve.

Caesar Salad

Serves 4

12 anchovy fillets
A little goat's or sheep's milk or
    unsweetened soya milk
1 egg
½ Cos lettuce

For the dressing:

2 tablespoons (36ml) olive oil
1 tablespoon (18ml) wine vinegar
Sea salt and freshly ground black pepper
1 garlic clove, crushed

For the croûtons:

2 slices bread, cubed
1-2 tablespoons (18–36ml) olive oil

1. Soak the anchovy fillets in goat's, sheep's or soya milk to make them less salty.
2. Put the egg in a saucepan of water and bring it to the boil, then cook the egg for 10 minutes. Run it under the cold tap and peel.
3. Rinse and spin the lettuce. Arrange the leaves in an upright position in a deep salad bowl.
4. Make the French dressing by stirring together the olive oil, vinegar, salt and pepper. Drop a crushed garlic clove into it. If you prefer a strong garlic flavour, make the dressing an hour or two ahead.
5. Make the croûtons by frying the cubed bread quickly in the olive oil on a high heat.
6. Chop the hard-boiled egg into small pieces and distribute it on the salad with the anchovies and croûtons.
7. Serve with French dressing passed around separately.

Watercress and Orange Salad _____ E W

Serves 4

This unusual salad is quick to make and attractive to the eye.

2 oz (55g) watercresss
2 oranges

1. Rinse the watercress and spin or pat it dry.
2. Peel the oranges and slice them thinly, reserving any spilled juice.
3. Arrange the watercress on a small platter and layer the orange slices on top, overlapping them slightly.
4. Dribble the reserved orange juice on top and serve.

Beetroot Salad _____ E W

Serves 4

People who usually find the taste of beetroot too strong may like this milder salad. If you substitute beetroot that is bought already cooked the taste will be sharper because of the added acetic acid.

6 oz (170g) fresh beetroot, scrubbed and sliced
4 oz (115g) carrots, scrubbed
6 oz (170g) dessert apples, peeled and quartered

1. Cook the sliced beetroot until tender, about 15 minutes. Let it cool.
2. Grate the cooked beetroot, raw carrot and apples by hand or in a food processor, using a shredding disc.
3. Stir the salad until evenly blended, put into a bowl and serve.

Beetroot and Hazel-nut Salad _____ E W

Serves 4

½ lb (225g) fresh beetroot, scrubbed and sliced
3 oz (85g) hazel-nuts
4 fl oz (12ml) sheep's or goat's milk yogurt
Sea salt and freshly ground black pepper

1. Cook the sliced beetroot.
2. Preheat the oven to 375°F/190°C (Gas Mark 5).
3. Put the hazel-nuts on a baking tray and roast them in the oven.
4. Rub the skins off the hazel-nuts.
5. Cut the cooked beetroot into cubes and allow it to cool.
6. Mix together the beetroot, hazel-nuts and yogurt. Season to taste and serve.

Greek Salad _____ E W

Serves 4

This is a very filling salad, so the servings are meant to be small.

4 oz (115g) Feta cheese
1 tomato
3 oz (85g) Greek black olives
Olive oil

1. Cut the cheese into ½-inch (1cm) cubes.
2. Slice the tomato into wedges, then cut the wedges in half.
3. Combine the cheese, tomato and olives in a small bowl and dribble olive oil on top.
4. Serve with other salads, or in individual portions on a bed of lettuce as a first course.

Cucumber and Yogurt Salad _____ E W

Serves 4

½ cucumber
A handful mint leaves (about 9)
6 tablespoons (108ml) sheep's or goat's
  milk yogurt

1. Peel, slice and cube the cucumber.
2. Rinse, dry and finely chop the mint
   leaves.
3. In a small bowl, mix together the
   cucumber, mint and yogurt.
4. Serve with other salads or as a cooling
   accompaniment to curry.

Waldorf Salad _____ E W

Serves 3

2 dessert apples
Lemon juice
1 stick celery
1 oz (30g) watercress
4 tablespoons (72ml) sheep's or goat's milk
  yogurt
1 oz (30g) sultanas or raisins

1. Chop the apples into small, bite-sized
   pieces. Do not peel them. Sprinkle a
   few drops of lemon juice over them to
   prevent discolouring.
2. Slice the celery crosswise.
3. Roughly chop the watercress, reserving
   a sprig or two for garnish.
4. In a small bowl, stir the yogurt and
   sultanas or raisins into the apples and
   vegetables.
5. Serve, decorated with watercress, or
   chill until required.

Courgette Coleslaw _____ W

Serves 4

The fresh chopped dill can be left out if there is none available.

For the salad:

½ lb (225g) cabbage
2 oz (55g) courgettes
2 oz (55g) carrots
1 stick celery
2 tablespoons (36ml) fresh parsley
Sea salt and freshly ground black pepper

For the dressing:

3 tablespoons (54ml) mayonnaise
3 tablespoons (54ml) sheep's or goat's milk
  yogurt
1 tablespoon (18ml) fresh dill, chopped

1. Rinse and shred the cabbage.
2. Slice the courgettes and leave them in rounds if they are small or quarter the rounds if the courgettes are big.
3. Scrub the carrots and grate them.
4. Dice the celery.
5. Finely chop the parsley.
6. Combine all the salad ingredients in a bowl and season.
7. Stir together the mayonnaise, yogurt and chopped dill.
8. Mix the dressing into the coleslaw and serve.

Potato Salad _____ W

Serves 4

Use all yogurt instead of the half mayonnaise/half yogurt mixture if an egg-free version is required. Potatoes are not high in calcium, so by increasing the yogurt you increase the calcium content of this salad.

1½ lb (680g) new potatoes or waxy old
  potatoes (e.g. Desirée)
Sea salt
½ teaspoon (3ml) onion, grated
2 tablespoons (36ml) mayonnaise
2 tablespoons (36ml) sheep's or goat's milk
  yogurt
Freshly ground black pepper
1 tablespoon (18ml) fresh chives or parsley,
  chopped

1. Scrub and slice the potatoes, and then cook them with salt until they are just tender. Cool.
2. Put the cooked potatoes in a bowl and stir in the grated onion, mayonnaise, yogurt and seasoning.
3. Mix in most of the chopped chives or parsley, reserving a little for sprinkling on top of the salad, and serve.

Carrot and Currant Salad _____ E W

Serves 4

A little French Dressing (see the recipe on page 122) can be mixed into this salad, if desired.

¾ lb (340g) carrots
3 oz (85g) currants

1. Scrub or peel the carrots and grate them. This can be done quickly in a food processor using a grating disc.
2. In a bowl, stir the currants into the grated carrots.
3. Serve with other salads, quiches, etc.

Three Bean Salad _____ E W

Serves 4

This salad tastes much better made from fresh ingredients rather than tinned, and it takes only a little more trouble to prepare.

2 oz (55g) kidney beans, soaked overnight
2 oz (55g) butter beans, soaked overnight
4 oz (115g) French beans
Sea salt
2 spring onions, sliced, including green parts
1 tablespoon (18ml) fresh parsley, chopped
Freshly ground black pepper
French Dressing, to taste (see the recipe on page 122).

1. Rinse the kidney and butter beans, bring them to the boil in 2 saucepans and cook them for 50 minutes. The kidney beans require 10 minutes of rapid boiling out of the 50.
2. Cook the French beans with a little salt until just tender.
3. Put all the beans in a 2-pint (1.4 litre) bowl. Stir in the chopped spring onions, parsley and pepper.
4. Serve with or without French Dressing, to taste.

Chinese Salad

Serves 6

2 oz (55g) green pepper, chopped, can take the place of the spring onions.

3 oz (85g) fresh beansprouts
6 oz (170g) Chinese leaves, shredded
1 stick celery, chopped
1 carrot, scrubbed and grated
2 oz (55g) mushrooms, sliced (optional)
4 spring onions, chopped
Freshly ground black pepper
French Dressing or Yogurt and Mayonnaise
    Dressing, to taste (see the recipes on
    pages 122 and 123)

1. Put the beansprouts in a bowl, pour boiling water on them and wait for 10 seconds. Drain.
2. In a shallow bowl, layer the shredded Chinese leaves, beansprouts, chopped celery, grated carrot (reserve a little bit), and mushrooms and spring onions.
3. Season with pepper, and grate the reserved carrot on top of the salad.
4. Serve with the dressing passed separately.

Pasta Salad

Serves 4

Sliced olives can be added.

For the dressing:

1 clove garlic
1 dessertspoon (12ml) wine vinegar
2 dessertspoons (24ml) olive oil

For the salad:

3 oz (85g) spiral pasta, weighed uncooked
Sea salt
2 oz (55g) French beans
2 oz (55g) carrots
1 oz (30g) red or green pepper
1 oz (30g) mushrooms
2 spring onions
1 tomato
1 dessertspoon (12ml) dill or other fresh
  herb
Freshly ground black pepper

1. Crush the garlic clove and combine with the vinegar and olive oil. Set the dressing aside to let the flavours combine while you prepare the rest of the salad.
2. Cook the pasta until *al dente* in lightly salted water. Drain.
3. Cut the French beans into 1 inch (2.5cm) pieces and dice the carrots. Lightly salt them and cook together until they are barely tender.
4. Dice the pepper, slice the mushrooms and spring onions, cut the tomato into eighths and chop the dill.
5. Let the cooked ingredients cool, then combine them with the raw vegetables.
6. Pour the dressing on, season and serve.

Tuna and Broccoli Pasta Salad

Serves 6–8

This recipe and the previous one for pasta salad taste better if they are made a few hours or even a day before serving.

4 oz (115g) broccoli, cut into florets
Sea salt
6 oz (170g) spiral pasta, weighed uncooked
1×6½-7½ oz (185-215g) tin tuna
4 spring onions, chopped, including the
  green parts
2 oz (55g) mushrooms, sliced
2 oz (55g) red or green pepper, chopped
2 oz (55g) pitted green olives, sliced
1 tablespoon (18ml) fresh parsley, chopped
Freshly ground black pepper
French Dressing (see the recipe on
  page 122)

1. Lightly salt the broccoli and cook it
   until it is just tender. Put it into a
   mixing bowl and leave it to cool.
2. In lightly salted water, boil the pasta
   until it is cooked *al dente*. Drain and
   allow it to cool, then mix it in with the
   broccoli.
3. Drain and flake the tuna and mix with
   the vegetables, parsley and seasoning.
4. Mix in French Dressing, to taste.

Rice Salad ———————————————— E W

Serves 6

Cooked kidney beans can be used in place of French beans.

7oz (200g) uncooked brown rice
Sea salt
4oz (115g) French beans, cut in small
  pieces
2 oz (55g) red pepper, sliced in small
  strips
3 spring onions, chopped, including the
  green parts
6 stoned green olives, sliced
1 tablespoon (18ml) fresh parsley, chopped
Freshly ground black pepper
French Dressing, to taste (see the recipe on
  page 122)

1. Cook the rice in boiling, salted water.
   Drain it and allow it to cool.
2. Cook the French beans until just
   tender. Cool.
3. Put the red pepper, spring onions,
   olives and parsley in a bowl.
4. Add the rice and French beans.
   Season with pepper.
5. Stir in French Dressing to taste, or
   serve the Dressing separately.

Courgette Salad _____ E W

Serves 3-4

5 oz (140g) courgettes
2 oz (55g) carrots
2 oz (55g) cauliflower
1 oz (30g) red pepper
Sea salt and freshly ground black pepper
French Dressing, to taste (see the recipe
    below)

1. Slice the courgettes thinly, then cut the slices into quarters.
2. Peel the carrots and grate them.
3. Remove a couple of florets from the head of the cauliflower and slice them thinly.
4. Slice the red pepper into small strips.
5. Combine all the vegetables, season, and mix in French Dressing, to taste.

French Dressing _____ E W

Serves 6

The proportions of this recipe will vary according to the specific vinegar you use, so it's a good idea to taste it before serving. Always be sure to use either red or white wine vinegar rather than malt vinegar. You can ring the changes by using wine vinegar infused with herbs, or by adding a teaspoon of French mustard or a crushed garlic clove. I always use olive oil because of its delicious taste, but sunflower oil makes an acceptable alternative.

2 tablespoons (36ml) wine vinegar
4 tablespoons (72ml) olive oil

1. Put the vinegar and olive oil in a screw top jar and shake it until the dressing is well mixed.
2. Serve in a small jug with a bowl underneath and a spoon at the side. The spoon may be needed to stir the dressing if it starts to separate.

Lemon and Yogurt Dressing _____ E W

Serves 4-6

6 tablespoons (108ml) sheep's or goat's
  milk yogurt
1 teaspoon (6ml) lemon juice
2 tablespoons (36ml) water

1. Combine all the ingredients and serve.

Tahini Dressing _____ E W

Serves 4

1 garlic clove, crushed
2 tablespoons (36ml) tahini
2 dessertspoons (24ml) lemon juice
4 dessertspoons (48ml) water, or more
Sea salt and freshly ground black pepper

1. Put the garlic clove in a small bowl,
   then add the tahini and lemon juice.
   Stir.
2. Gradually mix in the water. The
   amount you need to get the right
   consistency will vary depending on the
   thickness of the tahini.
3. Season and serve.

Yogurt and Mayonnaise Dressing _____ W

Serves 6

For a dill dressing, add 1 tablespoon (18ml) chopped fresh dill and a few drops of lemon juice.

3 tablespoons (54ml) sheep's or goat's milk
  yogurt
3 tablespoons (54ml) mayonnaise

1. Stir the yogurt and mayonnaise
   together.
2. Serve in a small bowl.

Russian Dressing _____ E W

Serves 4

6 tablespoons (108ml) sheep's or goat's
  milk yogurt
¼ teaspoon (1.5ml) chilli sauce
2 teaspoons (12ml) tomato ketchup

1. Combine all the ingredients.
2. Serve in a small bowl.

DESSERTS

There are many people who do not have a milk allergy who are interested in recipes for desserts made without cream. Sheep's and goat's milk yogurts work well in place of cream in mousse recipes or as a topping for puddings. The sorbet recipes in this chapter have such a smooth texture and refreshing taste that I think they would satisfy most people's yearning for ice cream. And who really needs to pour cream over lemon meringue pie, Bakewell tart, or cheesecake?

Note:
At the time of going to press, the Chief Medical Officer had issued a statement warning against the use of raw eggs in cooking in order to avoid possible salmonella poisoning. A few of the desserts in this chapter include raw eggs as an ingredient, but these recipes have been retained in the hope that in time the situation will be improved as a result of stricter feeding and monitoring controls in egg production.

Honey and Yogurt Parfait _____ E W

For each serving:

8 tablespoons (144ml) sheep's or goat's milk yogurt
2 teaspoons (12ml) clear honey
1 teaspoon (6ml) flaked almonds

1. In an individual dessert bowl or parfait glass, layer half the yogurt and half the honey.
2. Repeat.
3. Top with flaked almonds and serve.

Fruit Sorbet

Serves 6

If no food processor is available, omit step 2. Do not freeze the sorbet for 6 hours but rather for 2 or 3 hours, or until it is frozen to a mush. Stir it, freeze it for another ½ hour, then stir it again. Freeze until set.

4 oz (115g) granulated sugar
¼ pint (140ml) water
1 lb (455g) blackberries, raspberries, strawberries, plums or mulberries
1 egg white

1. Make a syrup by boiling the sugar in the water until the sugar dissolves. Cool.
2. In a food processor fitted with the metal blade, purée the fruit.
3. Sieve the fruit to remove seeds or skin.
4. Mix the fruit purée with the syrup in a bowl.
5. Beat the egg white until it forms soft peaks and fold it into the fruit syrup.
6. Put the mixture in a plastic container and freeze for at least 6 hours, or until it is set but still easy to chop up.
7. Break the sorbet up and put it into the bowl of the food processor fitted with the plastic blade. Process it until the sorbet turns a uniformly paler colour and increases in volume.
8. Freeze until set.
9. Thaw slightly and serve.

Mint Sorbet

Serves 4

3 oz (85g) sugar
½ pint (285ml) water
1 handful fresh mint leaves (about 9)
Juice of 1 lemon
1 egg white
A few sprigs mint, for garnish

1. Put the sugar and half the water in a saucepan. Boil until the sugar has dissolved completely.
2. Remove the syrup from the heat and pour in the other half of the water. Let it cool.
3. Put the mint leaves and the lemon juice into the bowl of a food processor fitted with the metal blade. Pour in some of the syrup, but not all of it, as it will probably overflow. Process for 5 seconds. Pour the rest of the syrup into the bowl.
4. In a small bowl, whisk the egg white. Fold the egg white into the mint syrup.
5. Freeze the sorbet for at least 6 hours, or until it is set but still easily broken up.
6. Break the sorbet up and put it into the bowl of the food processor fitted with the plastic blade and process until the sorbet increases in volume and turns bright white.
7. Freeze until set.
8. Top each serving with a sprig of mint.

Orange Soya Milk Ice 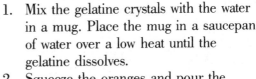 E W

Serves 6

This recipe, although not particularly high in calcium, is useful for someone who wants to eat ice cream but is allergic to dairy products, animal milks and eggs.

2 teaspoons (12ml) gelatine
2 tablespoons (36ml) water
2 oranges
4 oz (115g) granulated sugar
1½ pints (850ml) sweetened soya milk
1 teaspoon (6ml) real vanilla essence

1. Mix the gelatine crystals with the water in a mug. Place the mug in a saucepan of water over a low heat until the gelatine dissolves.
2. Squeeze the oranges and pour the juice into a mixing bowl.
3. Stir the sugar into the orange juice until it dissolves.
4. Add the soya milk, vanilla essence and gelatine mixture and stir well.
5. Put the mixture in a plastic container and freeze it until it is mushy (in a deep freeze this will take about 3½ hours).
6. Take the ice cream out of the freezer. If it has frozen hard, allow it to thaw slightly. Break it into pieces and either beat it by hand or whip it in a food processor, using the plastic blade.
7. Return the ice cream to the freezer and leave it there for about 2½ hours, or until it is mushy.
8. Beat it by hand or in a food processor.
9. Freeze until set and serve.

Chocolate Orange Mousse _____ W

Serves 3-4

4 oz (115g) plain chocolate
3 eggs, separated
Juice of 1 orange

1. Melt the chocolate in a small mixing bowl over hot but not boiling water. Remove from the heat and let it cool.
2. Beat the egg whites until they form soft peaks, then beat the yolks until they turn a paler colour.
3. Beat the egg yolks into the chocolate, a little at a time.
4. Beat the orange juice into the mixture.
5. Fold in the beaten egg whites.
6. Pour the mousse into a small soufflé dish or 3 to 4 ramekins. Chill until set, then serve.

Blackberry and Yogurt Mousse _____ W

Serves 4

Blackcurrants can be substituted for the blackberries. Omit the honey from the recipe, and cook the blackcurrants in 2 tablespoons (36ml) water with sugar to taste, then sieve. Melt the gelatine, then proceed with the rest of the recipe.

2 teaspoons (12ml) gelatine
2 tablespoons (36ml) water
8 oz (225g) fresh or frozen blackberries
2 tablespoons (36ml) honey
2 eggs, separated
1×8 oz (225g) carton sheep's or goat's milk yogurt

1. Mix the gelatine and the water in a mug and place the mug inside a saucepan of water on a low heat. Do not allow the water to boil. When the gelatine has dissolved, remove it from the heat and let it cool slightly.
2. Meanwhile make a fruit purée by pushing the blackberries through a sieve into a bowl. Discard the seeds. It helps to chop up the blackberries first in a food processor using the metal blade.
3. Stir the honey into the purée.

4. In a small bowl, whisk the egg whites until they form soft peaks. In another bowl, beat the egg yolks.
5. Stir the beaten egg yolks into the fruit purée, then slowly stir in the gelatine. Be sure that the fruit mixture is at room temperature before adding the gelatine, because the gelatine will begin to set and form lumps if the fruit mixture is too cold.
6. Fold in the yogurt and beaten egg whites.
7. Chill until set and serve.

Orange Mousse_____W

Serves 4–6

4 oranges
½ oz (15g) gelatine
4 tablespoons (72ml) water
3 eggs, separated
2 oz (55g) granulated sugar

1. Squeeze the oranges and pour the juice into a mixing bowl.
2. Mix the gelatine and the water in a mug and place it in a saucepan of water over a low heat until the gelatine has dissolved. Cool slightly.
3. Mix the egg yolks with the sugar and beat them with a wooden spoon until they turn pale in colour.
4. Whisk the gelatine solution with the egg yolks and sugar, and leave for about ten minutes, until it is beginning to set.
5. Beat the egg whites until they are stiff but not too dry, then fold them into the orange mixture with a metal spoon. Fold both sets ingredients together.
6. Transfer the mousse to a 2-pint (1.1 litre) casserole and chill until set, about 2½ hours, and serve.

Quick Fruit Dessert E W

Serves 4

You could try other combinations of fruit in this virtually instant pudding.

2 oranges
6 oz (170g) seedless grapes
2 bananas
4-6 oz (115-170g) sheep's or goat's milk
   yogurt

1. Peel and slice the oranges, chop them roughly, and divide them among 4 serving bowls.
2. Take the grapes off their stalks and add them to the oranges.
3. Just before serving, slice the bananas on top.
4. Pass the yogurt around so that everyone can help themselves.

Gooseberry Meringue W

Serves 4

1 lb (455g) gooseberries
Juice of 1 orange
1 oz (30g) granulated sugar, or to taste
2 egg whites
3 oz (85g) caster sugar

1. Preheat the oven to 350°F/180°C (Gas Mark 4).
2. Top and tail the gooseberries. Put them in a 1½-2-pint (850ml-1.1 litre) pie dish, and pour the orange juice and sugar on top.
3. Cover the gooseberries with foil and bake them in the oven for about 20 minutes, or until they have softened.
4. Whisk the egg whites until they form soft peaks, then beat in half of the caster sugar.
5. Fold in the rest of the sugar.
6. Spoon the meringue on top of the gooseberries.
7. Return the dish to the oven and bake for 10-15 minutes, or until the meringue is golden.

Orange 'Cheesecake' _____ E

Serves 6–8

This is a lighter dessert than the cherry cheesecake, and quicker to make. A 10½ oz (298g) tin mandarin oranges, drained, can be used when fresh clementines or tangerines are out of season.

For the base:

1½ oz (45g) margarine
4 oz (115g) wheatmeal biscuits

For the filling:

2 teaspoons (12ml) gelatine
2 tablespoons (36ml) water
1×8 oz (225g) tub sheep's or goat's
  milk yogurt
2 tablespoons (36ml) granulated
  sugar
4 fl oz (120ml) fresh orange juice
  from 1 or 2 oranges

For the topping:

3 clementines or 2 tangerines

1. Grease an 8-inch (20.5cm) cake tin with a detachable base.
2. Melt the margarine in a saucepan over a low heat.
3. Either put the biscuits in a plastic bag and use a rolling pin to crush them, or whizz them in a food processor, using the metal blade.
4. Stir the biscuit crumbs into the melted margarine.
5. Press the biscuit mix firmly on to the base and sides of the cake tin.
6. Put the gelatine in a mug and stir the water into it. Place the mug in a saucepan of water over a low heat. When the gelatine has dissolved let it cool for a few minutes.
7. Mix the yogurt, sugar and orange juice together. Add the gelatine mixture. Pour the filling into the biscuit crust.
8. Chill the cheesecake for a couple of hours until it is set.
9. Remove the rim of the tin, keeping the cheesecake on the base.
10. Arrange the clementine or tangerine segments in a circle around the rim of the cake and serve.

Bakewell Tart

Serves 6

For the pastry:

3½ oz (100g) flour
1½ oz (45g) Trex
Water

For the filling:

4-5 oz (115-140g) blackberry or
    blackcurrant jam
2 eggs
2 oz (55g) margarine
2 oz (55g) Muscovado sugar
6 oz (170g) ground almonds

1. Preheat the oven to 400°F/200°C
   (Gas Mark 6).
2. Rub the flour into the Trex until the
   mixture resembles breadcrumbs.
3. Moisten the pastry with enough water
   to make it hold together.
4. Roll the pastry out and line an 8-inch
   (20.5cm) quiche dish.
5. Spread the jam on the pastry base.
6. In a saucepan over a low heat, melt the
   margarine and Muscovado sugar.
7. Beat the eggs in a mixing bowl, then
   stir in the margarine and sugar
   mixture.
8. Fold in the ground almonds.
9. Pour the filling mixture into the pastry
   case.
10. Bake for 30 minutes, or until an
    inserted skewer comes out clean. *Freeze
    at this point if desired.*
11. Serve warm or cold.

Cherry Cheesecake

Serves 6

Fresh strawberries, raspberries or blackberries can be placed on top of this cheesecake with
or without a glaze. A mild, not too salty Feta cheese is best for this recipe.

For the base:

1½ oz (45g) margarine
4 oz (115g) digestive biscuits

1. Preheat the oven to 350°F/180°C
   (Gas Mark 4), and grease an 8-inch
   (20.5cm) cake tin with a detachable
   base.
2. Melt the margarine in a saucepan over
   a low heat.

For the filling:

5 oz (140g) Feta cheese
4 oz (115g) granulated sugar
4 tablespoons (72ml) sheep's or goat's milk
  yogurt
3 oz (85g) ground almonds
2 eggs, separated

For the topping:

1×15 oz (425g) tin stoned black cherries
¼ pint (140ml) juice reserved from the
  tinned cherries
1 teaspoon arrowroot

3. Either put the biscuits in a plastic bag
   and use a rolling pin to crush them, or
   whizz them in the bowl of a food
   processor, using the metal blade.
4. Stir the biscuit crumbs into the melted
   margarine.
5. Press the biscuit mix firmly onto the
   bottom and sides of the cake tin.
6. Finely grate the Feta cheese into a
   mixing bowl. Stir in the sugar, yogurt
   and ground almonds.
7. Beat the egg yolks and stir them into
   the cheese mixture, then whisk the egg
   whites until they form soft peaks and
   fold them in.
8. Pour the filling into the buiscuit crust
   and bake the cheesecake for about 40
   minutes, or until it is golden and set.
   Remove it from the oven and let it cool
   in the tin. *Freeze at this point if desired.*
9. Drain the cherries, reserving ¼ pint
   (140ml) of the juice for the glaze.
10. Make a paste with a tablespoon of the
    cherry juice and the arrowroot.
11. Heat the rest of the cherry juice over a
    low heat, and stir in the arrowroot
    mixture. Heat, stirring, until the glaze
    thickens.
12. Let the glaze cool slightly. Remove the
    rim of the cake tin, keeping the
    cheesecake on the base. Arrange the
    cherries on the cake, then pour the
    glaze on the fruit and cover the top of
    the cake with it.
13. Chill and serve.

Lemon Meringue Pie

Serves 6

The amount of sugar in this recipe can be reduced to taste.

For the pastry:

3½ oz (100g) flour
1½ oz (45g) Trex
Water

For the filling:

7 oz (200g) caster sugar
1½ oz (45g) cornflour
½ pint (285ml) water
1 oz (30g) margarine
5 tablespoons (90ml) lemon juice
3 egg yolks, beaten

For the meringue:

3 egg whites
1 oz (30g) caster sugar

1. Make the pastry by rubbing the fat into the flour and binding the mixture together with a little water. Then line an 8-inch (20.5cm) quiche or pie dish with it. Bake the pastry case blind (see note on page 99) at 400°F/200°C (Gas Mark 6), adding an extra 5–10 minutes to the usual cooking time to ensure that it is well baked. Let it cool. Keep the oven at the same setting.
2. Put the 7 oz (200g) caster sugar in a saucepan, and mix the cornflour into it. Gradually stir in the water.
3. Stir the cornflour mixture over a medium-low heat, using a wooden spoon, until the mixture comes to the boil. Let it boil for one minute, stirring rapidly.
4. Remove the pan from the heat and beat in the margarine and lemon juice.
5. Stir in the beaten egg yolks and cook the filling over a pan of boiling water until it is thick, stirring all the time. Let it cool. Spread the filling over the pastry base.
6. Whisk the egg whites until they are foamy but not stiff. Gradually beat in the caster sugar until the meringue is stiff and glossy.
7. Spread the meringue over the filling

and seal the pie around the edges.

8. Bake for 10–15 minutes, or until the meringue is golden and cooked.
9. Allow the pie to cool completely before serving it.

Danish Apple Pudding ———————————————— E

Serves 4

2 lb (900g) cooking apples
Water
2 tablespoons (36ml) honey
5 oz (140g) bread
2 oz (55g) margarine
3 oz (85g) demerara sugar
½ teaspoon (3ml) nutmeg
1 teaspoon (6ml) cinnamon
8 tablespoons (108ml) sheep's or goat's
  milk yogurt

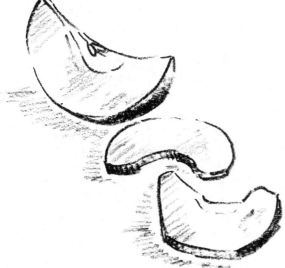

1. Peel and slice the apples and put them in a saucepan with a little water and the honey. Cook them until the apples are soft. Mash to a purée with a fork and leave to cool.
2. Put the bread in a food processor or liquidizer and turn it into breadcrumbs.
3. In a large non-stick frying pan, fry the breadcrumbs in the margarine until they are crisp.
4. When the breadcrumbs are cool, add the demerara sugar, nutmeg and cinnamon.
5. Lightly grease a 2-pint (1.1 litre) soufflé dish or a glass bowl.
6. Layer the breadcrumbs and apple purée, starting and finishing with breadcrumbs. *Freeze at this point if desired.*
7. Chill, if possible for 12 hours, as the flavour needs time to develop.
8. Serve the pudding, and pass around a bowl of yogurt to go with it.

Carrot Cake

Serves 8–10

For a better texture, I hand grate the carrots rather than grating them in the food processor. The walnuts can be left out, if there is someone in the house who objects to them. The butter cream seems to work well as a substitute for the usual cream cheese icing.

For the cake:

4 oz (115g) walnuts
6 fl oz (170ml) sunflower oil or corn oil
6 oz (170g) caster sugar
3 eggs
1 teaspoon (6ml) pure vanilla essence
½ lb (225g) carrots
6 oz (170g) self-raising flour
1 teaspoon (6ml) cinnamon

For the icing:

3 oz (85g) margarine
6 oz (170g) icing sugar, sifted
1 tablespoon (18ml) goat's milk or sheep's milk or sweetened soya milk
1 teaspoon (6ml) real vanilla essence

1. Preheat the oven to 400°F/200°C (Gas Mark 6). Grease an 8½-inch (21.5m) round spring clip tin, and dust it with flour.
2. Reserve 10 walnut halves for the top of the cake and roughly chop the rest.
3. Combine the oil, sugar, eggs and vanilla in a bowl. Beat well by hand.
4. Scrub the carrots and grate them coarsely by hand. Add them to the mixture.
5. Sift the flour with the cinnamon and stir into the cake mixture.
6. Pour the mixture into the prepared tin and bake for 55 minutes, or until an inserted skewer comes out clean.
7. Cool on a wire rack and turn out. *Freeze at this point if desired, and ice the cake when it has thawed.*
8. To make the icing, cream the margarine, then beat in the sifted icing sugar and moisten with the goat's or soya milk and vanilla. Alternatively, sift the icing sugar, then put it and the rest of the ingredients in a food processor using the plastic blade and process until smooth.

9. Ice just the top of the cake and decorate with the reserved walnut halves.

Blackberry and Apple Crumble ———————— E

Serves 4

The filling for Gooseberry Meringue (see page 130) can be used instead of blackberries and apples.

For the filling:

1½ lb (680g) apples
½ lb (225g) blackberries
2 tablespoons (36ml) honey, or to taste

For the crumble:

2 oz (55g) margarine
2 oz (55g) light brown sugar
4 oz (115g) self-raising white flour

1. Preheat the oven to 375°F/190°C (Gas Mark 5).
2. Peel and slice the apples and wash the blackberries. Put them in a 1½-pint (850ml) oval pie dish. Mix in the honey.
3. Put the fruit in the oven for about 15 minutes, or until the juices begin to run, then take it out of the oven.
4. Turn the oven up to 425°F/220°C (Gas Mark 7).
5. Rub in the ingredients for the crumble topping.
6. Distribute the crumble evenly over the fruit, and put the dish in the oven.
7. Bake for about 15 minutes, or until the crumble is golden and the fruit is bubbling.
8. Serve with plain sheep's or goat's milk yogurt, or with Yogurt Topping or Custard (see page 138).

Soya Milk Custard _____ W

Serves 6

If you use goat's milk instead of soya milk, omit the spices and vanilla.

1 pint (570ml) sweetened soya milk
2 eggs
1 tablespoon (18ml) cornflour
3 tablespoons (54ml) caster sugar
Pinch cinnamon
Pinch nutmeg
Pinch ginger
½ teaspoon (3ml) vanilla essence

1. Heat the milk gently in a saucepan.
2. In a mixing bowl, beat together the eggs, cornflour and sugar.
3. When the milk is warm but not quite boiling, pour it into the egg mixture and stir.
4. Pour the custard back into the saucepan cook over a medium-low heat, stirring continuously.
5. Add the spices and vanilla.
6. When the custard has thickened, pour it into a jug and serve.

Yogurt Topping _____ E W

Serves 4

4 oz (115g) sheep's or goat's milk yogurt
1 dessertspoon (12ml) pure maple syrup or honey

1. Mix the ingredients together. More or less maple syrup or honey can be used, to taste.
2. Serve in a bowl and pass around at the table.

CAKES, BISCUITS AND SNACKS

The cakes, biscuits and snacks in this chapter are made from carob, molasses, Muscovado sugar, nuts, dried fruit, cheese, self-raising flour and eggs.

Banana Date Loaf

Makes 1 loaf

2 oz (55g) margarine
2 oz (55g) Muscovado sugar
1 egg, beaten
4 oz (115g) self-raising flour, sieved
3 tablespoons (54ml) sheep's or goat's milk yogurt
1 banana, mashed
4 oz (115g) dried dates, chopped into small pieces

1. Preheat the oven to 325°F/170°C (Gas Mark 3), and grease a 1 lb (455g) loaf tin.
2. Cream the margarine and sugar, then stir in the egg alternately with the flour. Fold in the yogurt, mashed banana and chopped dates thoroughly. If using a food processor, beat the margarine, sugar, egg and flour in the bowl fitted with the plastic blade for one minute. Add the yogurt, banana and dates and process for another 15 seconds. Pour the mixture into the loaf tin.
3. Bake for about 1 hour, or until an inserted skewer comes out clean.
4. Cool in the tin and turn out.

Figgy Flapjacks E W

Serves 6

Dried apricots or dates can be substituted for the figs.

4 oz (115g) whole dried figs
3 oz (85g) margarine
3 tablespoons (54ml) golden syrup
6 oz (170g) porridge oats

1. Preheat the oven to 375°F/190°C (Gas Mark 5), and grease a 6-inch (15cm) square tin.
2. Chop the figs roughly and purée them in a food processor fitted with the metal blade.
3. Melt the margarine and syrup in a saucepan over a low heat.
4. Stir the porridge oats into the margarine and syrup, then stir the figs in thoroughly.
5. Spread the mixture over the cake tin. Bake for about 20 minutes or until golden.
6. Cut the flapjacks into 6 pieces while still warm. Allow them to cool before removing them.

Rock Cakes

Makes 18 cakes

These are wonderfully quick to make, and it takes no more time to bake a double batch. Rock cakes, like scones, are high in calcium owing to the self-raising flour and dried fruit.

8 oz (225g) self-raising flour
¼ teaspoon (1.5ml) cinnamon
4 oz (115g) sugar
4 oz (115g) margarine
4 oz (115g) currants
1 egg, beaten
A little goat's or sheep's milk or soya milk

1. Preheat the oven to 425°F/220°C (Gas Mark 7), and grease 18 depressions in two patty tins.
2. Combine the flour, cinnamon and sugar in a bowl and rub in the margarine.
3. Stir in the currants.
4. Put the beaten egg into a measuring jug and pour in enough milk to make the liquid up to 3 fl oz (90ml). Stir the egg and milk into the flour mixture until it collects together the lumps.
5. Spoon the mixture into the tins. It will seem quite dry at this point, but the separate lumps will fuse during baking.
6. Bake for 15–20 minutes, or until golden.
7. Cool in the tins and then turn out.

Apricot Scones

Makes 10-12

This is a variation of the usual fruit scone recipe, in which 2 oz (55g) currants take the place of the apricots. Try to find naturally dried apricots.

2 oz (55g) dried apricots
2 teaspoons (12ml) baking powder
Dash salt
½ lb (225g) self-raising flour
2 oz (55g) margarine
1 oz (30g) granulated sugar
1 egg
A little goat's or sheep's milk or soya milk

1. Preheat the oven to 425°F/220°C (Gas Mark 7) and grease 2 baking trays.
2. Chop the dried apricots into small cubes the size of currants.
3. Add the baking powder and salt to the flour.
4. Rub the margarine into the flour mixture. Stir in the sugar and fruit.
5. In a measuring jug, whisk the egg, then add enough milk to make the liquid up to ¼ pint (104ml). Stir it into the mixture.
6. Lightly roll the dough out on a floured surface and cut out 10-12 scones with a 2-inch (5cm) cutter. Place them on the trays.
7. Bake for 15 minutes, or until the scones are risen and golden.
8. Slide the scones onto a wire rack to cool.
9. Serve with margarine.

Wholesome Mincemeat _____ E W

Makes 1¾ lb (1.2kg), enough for 40 mince pies

This version is much lower in fat and sugar than commercially produced mincemeat. The apples and carrots provide sweetness, and most of the content is fruit, rather than sugar and suet. The flavour is so delicious that by comparison the bought varieties seem sickly sweet.

½ lb (225g) dessert apples, peeled and grated
4 oz (115g) carrots, grated
4 oz (115g) raisins
4 oz (115g) currants
4 oz (115g) sultanas
2 oz (55g) Muscovado sugar
2 oz (55g) beef suet
1 teaspoon (6ml) mixed spice
2 tablespoons (36ml) sherry or brandy, to taste

1. Grate the apples and carrots by hand or in a food processor.
2. Combine all the ingredients.
3. Use immediately or put in a container in the refrigerator where it can be used as required over 2 or 3 weeks. If frozen, it will keep for a year.

Mince Pies

Makes 22

8 oz (225g) self-raising flour
4 oz (115g) margarine
Water
15 oz (425g) Wholesome Mincemeat (see
   the recipe on page 143)
A little goat's or sheep's milk or soya milk

1. Preheat the oven to 425°F/220°C
   (Gas Mark 7) and grease 2 patty tins.
2. Rub the flour into the margarine and
   dribble in enough water to make the
   pastry moist.
3. Roll out the pastry on a floured
   surface, cut out 22 rounds with a
   cutter and line the depressions in the
   tins.
4. Generously fill the pastry rounds with
   mincemeat.
5. Cut 22 smaller rounds of pastry for the
   lids, prick them with a fork, and place
   them on top of the mincemeat. Do not
   seal the edges.
6. Glaze the mince pies with goat's,
   sheep's or soya milk.
7. Bake for about 15 minutes, or until
   golden.
8. Cool the pies in the tins, then turn out.

Mincemeat Cake

Serves 6

The honey in this cake will make it sink a bit, but it helps to make it very moist.

4 oz (115g) self-raising flour
1 teaspoon baking powder
2 eggs
4 oz (115g) margarine
1 tablespoon (18ml) honey
2 tablespoons (36ml) goat's or sheep's milk or soya milk
7 oz (200g) Wholesome Mincemeat (see the recipe on page 143)

1. Preheat the oven to 375°F/190°C (Gas Mark 5). Grease a 7- or 8-inch (18 or 20.5cm) round tin and dust it with flour.
2. Sift together the flour and baking powder.
3. If you are making the cake by hand, beat the eggs. Cream the margarine and honey, then alternately beat in the flour and baking powder and the eggs. Stir in the milk and fold in the mincemeat. If you are using a food processor, put the sifted flour and baking powder, margarine, honey, eggs and milk in the bowl fitted with the plastic blade. Beat for 45 seconds, add the mincemeat and beat for a further 15 seconds.
4. Spread the mixture in the cake tin. Bake for 30–40 minutes, or until an inserted skewer comes out clean.
5. Cool in the tin and turn out.

Irish Soda Bread

Makes 1 loaf

1 lb (455g) plain flour
1 teaspoon (6ml) baking soda
1 teaspoon (6ml) baking powder
1 teaspoon (6ml) salt
1½ oz (45g) margarine
7 oz (200g) raisins
8 fl oz (240ml) goat's or sheep's milk or soya milk
2 teaspoons (12ml) lemon juice
1 egg, beaten

1. Preheat the oven to 375°F/190°C (Gas Mark 5) and grease a baking tray.
2. Put the flour in a mixing bowl, and stir in the baking soda, baking powder and salt.
3. Rub in the margarine. Add the raisins.
4. Sour the milk with the lemon juice, then stir it into the mixture with the beaten egg.
5. On a floured surface, knead the dough very lightly, shaping it into a flattish round about 1 inch (2.5cm) thick.
6. Lay the dough on the greased baking tray, and using a wet knife, cut a cross on top.
7. Bake for 35 minutes or until well risen and brown.
8. Cool on a wire rack and serve in slices with or without margarine.

Tahini Cookies

Makes 30

2½ oz (70g) Trex
3 oz (85g) Muscovado sugar
5 oz (140g) self-raising flour
1 egg, beaten
3 oz (85g) tahini
1 teaspoon (5ml) vanilla essence

1. Preheat the oven to 350°F/180°C (Gas Mark 4). Grease 3 baking trays.
2. Cream the Trex and sugar, beat in the flour and egg and stir in the tahini and vanilla. Alternatively, put all the ingredients in a food processor fitted with the plastic blade, and beat for 45 seconds.
3. Place in heaped teaspoonfuls on the greased trays.
4. Bake for about 12 minutes, or until firm and golden.

Cherry Almond Cake

Serves 6

4 oz (115g) margarine
2 oz (55g) Muscovado sugar
3 eggs
4 oz (115g) ground almonds
1 oz (30g) self-raising flour
2 teaspoons (12ml) pure vanilla essence
4 oz (115g) natural glacé cherries, cut in
half

1. Preheat the oven to 350°F/180°C
   (Gas Mark 4). Grease a 7-inch (18cm)
   cake tin and dust it with flour.
2. If you are making the cake by hand,
   cream the margarine and sugar in a
   mixing bowl. Whisk the eggs and stir
   them into the mixture alternately with
   the ground almonds. Fold in the flour,
   vanilla essence and cherries. If you are
   using a food processor, put the first six
   ingredients in the bowl fitted with the
   plastic blade. Process for 50 seconds.
   Add the cherries and whizz for
   10 seconds.
3. Turn into the prepared tin and bake
   the cake for 35–50 minutes, or until an
   inserted skewer comes out clean.
4. Cool in the tin. Run a knife around the
   edges and turn out on a wire rack.

Almond Biscuits   E W

Makes 30 biscuits

This is an unusual biscuit recipe because it has no eggs or flour.

3 oz (85g) margarine
3 oz (85g) icing sugar, sifted
5 oz (140g) ground almonds

1. Preheat the oven to 375°F/190°C
   (Gas Mark 5), and grease 2 baking
   trays.
2. Cream the margarine and sifted icing
   sugar together, then stir in the ground
   almonds. Alternatively blend all the
   ingredients in a food processor, fitted
   with the plastic blade, for 30 seconds.
3. Drop heaped teaspoonfuls of the
   mixture onto the baking trays and bake
   for 10–15 minutes, or until golden.

Carob Fudge Cake _____ E

Serves 9

In my experience a straight substitution of carob for chocolate doesn't work. This combination of carob and Caro is the closest I've got to a chocolate taste, and it really is delicious. It's ideal for someone who has an allergy to chocolate but adores the taste. For some unknown reason, carob fudge cake tastes better the day after it is baked.

¾ lb (340g) self-raising flour
1 teaspoon (6ml) baking powder
3 tablespoons (54ml) carob powder
3 tablespoons (54ml) Caro barley drink granules
6 oz (170g) granulated sugar
10 tablespoons (180ml) vegetable oil
1 tablespoon (18ml) wine vinegar
1½ teaspoons (7.5ml) real vanilla essence
16 fl oz (485ml) water

1. Preheat the oven to 350°F/180°C (Gas Mark 4). Line an 8-inch (20.5cm) square tin with a detachable base, using greased, greaseproof paper.
2. Put the unsieved self-raising flour in a big mixing bowl. Sift the baking powder on top of it.
3. Push the carob and Caro through a sieve into the bowl. Mix the sugar in.
4. Make three wells in the dry ingredients, and pour oil in one, vinegar in the next, and vanilla in the third.
5. Keep stirring while gradually pouring in the water. Turn the mixture into the cake tin.
6. Bake for 40–50 minutes. The cake is done when it is shrinking away from the sides, but don't worry if an inserted skewer doesn't come out completely clean — it is a fudge cake after all.
7. Cool in the tin and turn out.
8. Ice the top of the cake with Carob Icing (see the next recipe).

Carob Icing _____ E W

This amount of icing is enough for the top of the Carob Fudge Cake in the previous recipe.

2 oz (55g) margarine
2 oz (55g) icing sugar
1 tablespoon (18ml) carob powder
1 tablespoon (18ml) Caro barley drink granules
2 teaspoons (12ml) hot water
1 teaspoon (6ml) real vanilla essence

1. Cream the margarine in a small bowl, then sieve the icing sugar into it. Beat them together.
2. In a smaller bowl, sieve the carob powder and Caro.
3. Mix the carob and Caro to a paste with the hot water. Add the vanilla.
4. Beat the carob mixture into the margarine and icing sugar until smooth.

Cheese Loaf _____

Makes 1 loaf

This loaf can be sliced and spread with margarine, but it is really moist enough as it is.

½ lb (225g) self-raising flour
1 teaspoon (6ml) dry English mustard
½ teaspoon (3ml) salt
3 oz (85g) Feta cheese, coarsely grated
1 egg
5 tablespoons (90ml) sheep's or goat's milk yogurt
6 tablespoons (108ml) goat's or sheep's milk or unsweetened soya milk

1. Grease a 2 lb (1kg) loaf tin and preheat the oven to 350°F/180°C (Gas Mark 4).
2. Sift the self-raising flour, mustard and salt into a bowl. Add the grated cheese.
3. In another bowl, whisk together the egg and yogurt, then gradually incorporate the milk.
4. Beat the two mixtures together and pour the loaf mix into the tin.
5. Bake for 50 minutes, or until an inserted skewer comes out clean.
6. Cool in the tin, slice round the edges and turn out.

Cheese Scones

Makes 10-12

½ lb (225g) self-raising flour
2 teaspoons (12ml) baking powder
Dash salt
2 oz (55g) margarine
2 oz (55g) Feta cheese, coarsely grated
1 teaspoon (6ml) French mustard
¼ pint (140ml) goat's or sheep's milk or
   unsweetened soya milk.

1. Preheat the oven to 425°F/220°C (Gas Mark 7), and grease 2 baking trays.
2. Put the flour in a mixing bowl and add the baking powder and salt to it.
3. Rub the margarine into the flour mixture.
4. Stir in the cheese, mustard and milk.
5. Lightly roll the dough on a floured surface and cut out 10-12 scones with a 2-inch (5cm) cutter. Place them on the trays.
6. Bake for about 15 minutes, or until the scones are risen and golden.
7. Serve with or without margarine.

Carob Chip Cookies

Makes 32

Some carob drops are dark in colour and very bitter. Try to find the lighter, sweeter type, but make sure they do not contain milk.

3 oz (85g) margarine
2 oz (55g) Muscovado sugar
1 egg
½ teaspoon (3ml) real vanilla essence
6 oz (170ml) self-raising flour
4 oz (115g) carob drops, quartered

1. Preheat the oven to 350°F/180°C (Gas Mark 4), and grease two baking trays.
2. Cream the margarine and sugar, and beat in the egg and vanilla essence.
3. Sift the flour and stir it into the mixture. Fold in the chopped carob drops. Alternatively put the margarine, sugar, egg, vanilla essence and flour into a food processor and blend for

1 minute. Add the chopped carob
pieces and process for another
15 seconds.

4. Place in teaspoonfuls on the greased
   baking trays.
5. Bake for 15 minutes, or until firm and
   golden. Cool on wire trays.

Orange Carob Chip Cake

Makes 1 loaf

3 oz (85g) margarine
½ lb (225g) self-raising flour
3 oz (85g) Muscovado sugar
4 oz (115g) carob drops or carob bar
Juice of 1 orange
A little goat's or sheep's milk or soya milk
1 egg
1 teaspoon (6ml) pure vanilla essence

1. Preheat the oven to 350°F/180°C
   (Gas Mark 4), and grease a 2 lb (1kg)
   loaf tin.
2. Rub the margarine into the flour in a
   mixing bowl.
3. Rub in the Muscovado sugar.
4. Quarter the carob drops or cut the
   carob bar into small pieces and stir
   them into the dry ingredients.
5. Squeeze the orange and pour the juice
   into a measuring jug. Pour in enough
   goat's, sheep's or soya milk to make the
   liquid up to ¼ pint (140ml).
6. Beat the egg, and pour it in. Stir in the
   orange juice, milk and vanilla essence.
7. Pour the mixture into the greased loaf
   tin and bake for about one hour, or
   until an inserted skewer comes out
   clean.
8. Cool on a wire rack and turn out.
   Serve in slices.

Gingerbread

Serves 9

You may find it easier to measure the molasses and syrup in tablespoons. Use 1 tablespoon for each ounce. The molasses and Muscovado sugar in this recipe make it a high-calcium cake.

4 oz (115g) margarine

2 oz (55g) golden syrup

4 oz (115g) black strap molasses or black treacle

4 oz (115g) Muscovado sugar

10 oz (285g) self-raising flour

2 teaspoons (12ml) ground ginger

1 teaspoon (6ml) cinnamon

1 teaspoon (6ml) baking powder

1 egg, beaten

7 fl oz (200ml) goat's or sheep's milk or soya milk

1. Preheat the oven to 300°F/150°C (Gas Mark 2). Using greased greaseproof paper, line a 9-inch (23cm) square tin with a removable base.

2. Melt the margarine, syrup, molasses or treacle, and the Muscovado sugar in a saucepan over a low heat. Let the mixture cool slightly.

3. Sieve the flour, ginger, cinnamon and baking powder straight into the mixture in the saucepan. Stir in well.

4. Stir the beaten egg and milk into the other ingredients.

5. Pour the cake mix into the prepared tin and bake for 1 hour, or until an inserted skewer comes out clean.

6. Keeping the cake on the base, remove the tin and stand the gingerbread on a wire rack. Serve cut in squares, either at room temperature or hot with custard as a pudding (see the recipe on page 138).

Parkin

Makes 18 fingers

Parkin improves by being stored in a tin.

1 teaspoon (6ml) bicarbonate of soda
¼ pint (140ml) goat's or sheep's milk or
  soya milk
4 oz (115g) Trex
6 tablespoons (108ml) pure cane molasses
  or black treacle
4 tablespoons (72ml) honey
½ lb (225g) porridge oats or oatmeal
½ lb (225g) wholemeal self-raising flour
2 teaspoons (12ml) ginger

1. Preheat the oven to 325°F/160°C
   (Gas Mark 3).
2. Using greased greaseproof paper, line
   an 8-inch (20.5cm) square tin with a
   removable base.
3. Dissolve the bicarbonate of soda in the
   milk.
4. Melt the Trex, molasses or treacle and
   honey in a large saucepan over a
   medium-low heat.
5. Stir the porridge oats, flour, ginger and
   milk mixture into the other ingredients.
6. Turn the mixture into the lined tin and
   bake for 50–60 minutes, or until an
   inserted skewer comes out clean.

American Corn Bread or Muffins

Makes 2×8-inch (20.5cm) square cakes or 12 muffins
The muffins are delicious served warm with margarine at breakfast.

1 oz (30g) margarine
4 oz (115g) granulated sugar
1 egg, beaten
5 oz (140g) self-raising flour
7 oz (200g) cornmeal
8 fl oz (240ml) goat's or sheep's milk or soya milk

1. Preheat the oven to 400°F/200°C (Gas Mark 6). Grease two 8-inch (20.5cm) baking tins or an American deep muffin tin with 12 deep depressions.
2. To make the mixture by hand or with an electric beater, cream the margarine and sugar, then add the egg and beat together. Sift the flour and cornmeal together twice and add them to the creamed mixture alternately with the milk. If using a food processor, put the margarine, sugar and egg in the bowl fitted with the plastic blade, and beat for 30 seconds. Add the twice-sifted flour and cornmeal, and then the soya milk. Beat for another 30 seconds.
3. Bake the bread for 35 minutes and the muffins for 30 minutes, or until an inserted skewer comes out clean.

WHOLESOME SNACKS
Walnut-stuffed Dates _____ E W

Children like to make these themselves. Simply chop the stalks off some dried dates and slit them along one side. Remove the stones and insert either walnut pieces or a whole almond.

Carob Raisin Nut Snack _____ E W

Mix equal parts sweetened (but milk-free) carob chips, raisins and blanched peanuts.

Popcorn E W

Makes 1 enormous bowlful

I have included this recipe because it is a cheap, low-calorie, nourishing food which makes a change from crisps and expands the range of permissible snacks in a milk-free diet. Older children like making it themselves.

2 tablespoons (36ml) oil
6 oz (170g) popping corn
Salt (optional)

1. Coat the bottom of a 7-pint (4 litre) capacity saucepan with the oil.
2. Put 4 kernels of corn in the pan.
3. Cover the pan and put it on a high heat. Each kernel will make a loud pop when cooked. When all 4 have popped the oil is the right temperature.
4. Put the rest of the corn in the pan, cover, and agitate the pan by sliding it back and forth over a medium-high heat until there are no more pops. Don't raise the lid too early.
5. Lift the lid off the saucepan — the popcorn will have filled it.
6. Sprinkle salt on the popcorn and serve in 1 large or 2 smaller bowls.

IDEAS FOR PACKED LUNCHES

The following sandwich fillings can be used on a variety of breads or buns:

salmon and cucumber
Pilchard and Tomato Spread (see page 36)
Sardine Pâté (see page 35)
Special Tuna Salad (see page 66)
chicken, watercress and mayonnaise
American Chicken Salad (see page 84)
egg salad made with ½ yogurt and ½ mayonnaise, and cress
   tahini and honey
minced tofu and sprouting seeds
peanut butter

You can also include the following quiches:

Broccoli Quiche (see page 100)
Leek Quiche (see page 99)
Mushroom Quiche (see page 100)
Roquefort Quiche (see page 101)
Tuna and Cucumber Quiche (see page 64)
Salmon and Cheese Quiche (see page 63)
Spinach Quiche (see page 102)

Salads that will stand up to travelling include:

Three Bean Salad (see page 118)
Potato Salad (see page 117)
Pasta Salad (see page 120)
Tuna and Broccoli Pasta Salad (see page 120)

Vegetables and fruit:

celery sticks
carrot sticks
olives

oranges
tangerines
raisins
grapes

Sheep's or goat's milk fruit yogurts (if these are not available in your area you could mix the
fruit in yourself)

Sheep's or goat's milk cheese and biscuits

A choice from the Cakes, Biscuits and Snacks section (see pages 139-155)

INDEX

(E) = egg-free recipes
(W) = wheat-free recipes

159